Kids in Clover

Kids in Clover

Jill Gill and the
team at Clover House

The Clover House way of improving children's lives

Quicksilver Publications

First published by Quicksilver Publications in the United Kingdom
in 2015 on behalf of Clover House. www.cloverhouse.org

Copyright © Clover House 2015
This edition published 2015

ISBN – 978-0-9932872-1-3 – soft cover
ISBN – 978-0-9932872-3-7 – hard cover

Type set in Palatino 12 point
Origination by Patricia J Mills
Printed and bound by Henry Ling Ltd, Dorchester.

Acknowledgements

Jill Gill co-founded Clover House in 1996, working as Practise Manager and, for over 12 years, as a Massage Therapist. The case studies in this book have been collected and composed by Jill from the therapist's notes.

Contributing imagery therapists are Basil Jones, co-founder and original imagery therapist; John Forster who proved we help children within three sessions; and Jo Coles.

Nutritionists include Carole Taylor, Elaine Newcombe Jones and Philippa Parish, who has been with us for almost 10 years. Our Massage therapists were Amie Budd, Kym Roberton and Carla Jo Gerherty.

Inevitably not all therapists have the same training, experience, or way of working, but they have formed a great team, and found successfully treating so many children both rewarding and satisfying.

Our thanks go to the parents and children who put our advice into practice, and to all those who gave us feedback and permission to include their thank you letters.

As a Charity, our greatest thanks of course go to the Trustees, Rob Walsh, David O'Hagan and Jackie Marsh who supported this publication, and last but not least, to all the funders and donors who have enabled us to learn, share and care for the children coming to Clover House.

Contents

Preface

The Medicine
of Compassion

In a film called the *The Medicine of Compassion*, Simon Fox talks with Candice Pert (author of *Everything You Need to Know to Feel Good*) explains how compassion can heal.

'When a sick person senses the care of another human being, their physiology changes: blood flow increases, heartbeat slows, and breathing is enhanced, resulting in a healing state that we can readily see.

'When receptors vibrating the tiny channels connecting the cell surface to its interior open and close, it allows ions to flow in and out of the cell.'

In his teaching about compassion, Simon says, 'This caring doesn't take place in what the Greeks called 'chronos' or normal linear time. Instead it occurs in 'kyros' or non-linear time. When patients sense that someone actually cares about them and their suffering, then a sudden quantum shift occurs. Compassion is a quantum event, something that happens instantaneously.

'My point is that it doesn't take any more time for professionals to be compassionate in their interactions than it does for them to be perfunctory and routine.

'What we are saying is that this caring is a deep, synchronizing vibration that, when resonant, produces a sudden shift to bring about a coherent, healing state that happens in almost no time at all.'

Chapter 1

The Story Behind Clover House

When we answer the telephone to a mother who is explaining the problems with their child and often desperate to know if we can help – what ever the complaint, the chances are we can.

For over 18 years, Clover House has been seeing any child with any complaint or problem, and our records show that over 75% of them experience improvement or alleviation of their problems and condition. We state we can help with any physical, emotional or behavioural problem, but of course every child and family is different. However the programme from Clover House is the same.

The family attends for a recommended three sessions, and each session consists of seeing three therapists or therapies in turn. These are nutrition, massage and imagery.

With nutrition, we simply explain that every single cell in the body can only work by receiving nutrients. By improving a child's nutrition they can feel better, have more energy and boost the immune system. Supplements and vitamins can also help heal the body, or condition.

With massage, a parent can give a very active form of tender loving care to their child, increasing the bonding and feel-good hormones, as well as helping relaxation and sleep.

Imagery uses the mind. Considering we are mainly operated by the subconscious, it makes sense to access and use it. The mind does not know the difference between fantasy and reality. Imagery techniques can alleviate fears, phobias, anxieties, worries, bad memories or traumas, unhelpful habits, thoughts and emotions. These techniques can be done in minutes.

The combination of three therapies accelerates and enhances the results. But with most complementary medicine, the responsibility and the work involves the parent and the child. We know that if our nutritional advice is followed, such as having proper breakfasts, meals and snacks with lots of protein, if they give some massage to their child, and the child practises the mind techniques given to them – by the next week or next session, things will have improved.

A quick example from the early days of how each therapy works together came from a mother with a young child of about 3, who had problems with constipation. It had continued despite visits to the doctor, a consultant and A & E at hospital. The whole extended family was suffering – Mum could not take the child out as she was lifeless and sitting on the floor, trying to stop going to the toilet and in fear of pain; Grandad had verbally lashed out saying it wasn't right; Mum felt victimised for being accused of getting the child to have water and Weetabix (which she had); and they had had many prescriptions for laxatives which seemed to make the matter worse.

At the first session with the nutritionist Mum was advised to replace cow's milk with goat's milk, which is more similar to human milk, and she was given some ideas on how to introduce nutritional foods. With massage, Mum was shown how to rub the abdomen, and the feet using reflexology, helping the digestive tract.

With imagery, the child, although very young, was captivated by recently seeing a Disney Tarzan movie – and was told a story about how Tarzan had to go to the toilet in the trees, and making it fun and funny (thereby decreasing the fear). Mum was amazed and relieved to find the problem was alleviated that same evening, and by the third session was completely cured.

From a simple complaint to more complex and serious medical conditions such as Crohn's disease, help is at hand. A 16-year-old came with his Mum who was at her wits end. Her son was suffering such a restricted life; he didn't go to school much, he sat watching his friends from the window. His condition meant he was in pain, and on a lot of medication. He had to be near a toilet for numerous visits each day and throughout the night. Family life had revolved around his condition for years. He had been hospitalised and the family was exhausted, with the next step an operation to remove much of his colon.

The family and the young man were able to increase nutrients and aid healing with specific helpful foods, vitamins and minerals, and to decrease and eliminate some powerful medication that was causing serious side effects.

Mum reported that as well as helping ease her son's suffering, she was able to give him quality time and help her other children with massage. With special metaphoric imagery the young man imagined his pain coming from knives, and how the knives were destroyed, which in turn alleviated the pain.

Although it took longer than three sessions, after one month he was pain free, and later we were visited by the young man to show off his motorbike and then a car, and we were told he went to college. When followed up by a member of staff years later, he said he had never told his girlfriend he had even had the condition.

Despite our advanced scientific, technical and educated society – children are suffering more. This last year head teachers have reported they are worried about the high levels of anxiety-associated problems in children. Increasing levels of self harm among youngsters are being exposed. Teachers report that they experience pupils suffering from being overweight, underweight, and with eating disorders. They see behavioural problems leading to specific diagnosis, leading to increased expense, medication, and exclusions and expulsions from school. Chronic conditions such as asthma and eczema persist.

It makes sense to have tried-and-tested methods, or even to return to old fashioned ways, to offer safe, natural and effective self help. Clover House has delivered a programme of nutrition, massage and imagery very efficiently and effectively which has successfully helped many hundreds of children and families. The results of the past eighteen years have led to the publication of this book, and in accordance with its charitable aims, to publish the results widely.

Chapter 2

How It Works

Clover House Complementary Therapy Centre for children was set up as a charity in 1996 with the aim 'to relieve sickness and suffering of children and young people through the provision of complementary care, and to publish the results widely'.

It is run from a bungalow, deliberately a home from home, so that parents and children can feel at ease. The child is the main focus of attention and the child is seen as an individual – not in terms of a label or condition.

Behaviour is not seen as 'bad' or 'naughty' – but as an expression of distress. The aim is for the child to have an enjoyable experience, and everyone is easy going and relaxed. This enables parents and children to focus, hear, understand and feel free to question. In fact the most repeated evaluation is 'friendly but professional', and most parents are agreeably surprised at the level of information and experience, advice, practical help and support.

The idea is to work alongside parents and children to assist and motivate them to use self help techniques of each of the three disciplines at home. For life. An essential factor is using the techniques. Often quoted to parents is the maxim, 'If you keep doing what you keep doing, you keep getting what you keep getting' and also, 'What you put in is what you get out.'

The Procedure

There is no formal referrals procedure. The majority of parents have been recommended by other parents – word of mouth. There is a questionnaire to complete, to save time and avoid the child having to hear repeated negativity of their behaviour or a lengthy history of their illness. There are questions such as when the condition became apparent, what other treatments have been tried, or other professionals involved, and what the possible causes might be.

Parents are free to write as much or as little as they want, including comments on pregnancy, birth and thereafter. Some nutritional questions include space to list all foods and drinks consumed over the past four days.

When the questionnaire has been returned, we suggest a donation fee, without which we find appointments are not kept. This fee is currently about one third of commercial fees. An appointment is usually available within a week or two.

The suggestion and expectation is for three sessions, being the average for change and improvement. Parents are free to choose less or more sessions. Each family is booked into a two-hour slot, generally allowing 30–40 minutes for each visit to three different therapists in three separate consulting rooms.

Goals or Scores

Children or parents are asked what they want to achieve and to score the symptoms or goals out of 10 (the lower the score the worse the condition, symptom or problem). Scores are recorded at each visit in order to monitor progress.

Each therapist will explain their particular therapy, and with discussion, will be able to give individually tailored advice, instructions, practical demonstrations where applicable, and give handouts. With nutrition, vitamins and supplements might be prescribed. With massage, a handout, oils, an individual flower remedy, and a relaxing children's CD provided. The therapists make notes. A file is created for each child with their goal sheet and, if possible, follow-up scores after the third session. A case study is completed so that prospective parents can read about other anonymous children with similar problems.

Chapter 3

Why Nutrition?

Our bodies are made and maintained from what we eat. Every 16 days about 72% of our cells are replaced. The surface cells of digestion are renewed every five minutes; red blood cells in 120 days; the stomach every four days; the liver in six weeks; the heart every six months; bones are replaced over 10 years. We are primarily made of what we have eaten during the past year.

What cells need

For cells to stay healthy they require a constant supply of nutrients, water, fresh air, and the ability to dispose of waste material. The foods we eat contain nutrients. Nutrients come in the form of vitamins, minerals, hydrocarbons, water, enzymes, amino acids and fats. These nutrients sustain life by providing the basic materials the body needs to carry out its daily functions – including combatting infection, repairing tissue and even simply thinking. Under stress we use up more essential nutrients just to keep going.

Extent of poor nutrition

It is estimated that about 3% of the western population eats a healthy balanced diet, and even then some of them are lacking in vital nutrients. The problem is that we do not get what we need from our 'modern diet'.

Maurice Hanssen, Director of the Council for Responsible Nutrition, was reported as saying, 'Until 4,000 years ago, the average human diet contained about 225 different foods. Today, 90% of our average calorie intake comes from just 18 foods. The majority of people are lacking in virtually every vitamin and mineral.'

Nutritionists advocate getting nutrients from food first, but today studies have shown there are less nutrients in our soil, and consequently in harvested foods too.

Poor habits learned at home

Studies have shown that poor eating habits are learned in the home. Diets low in vegetables and high in preservatives are served in the home and at school, and parents do not take the time to cook healthy meals for their children, which leads to poor dietary decisions later in life.

Consequences of poor nutrition

Diet and nutrition affect how we look, feel, think and behave. How we fuel our bodies dictates how well our body can perform emotionally, physically and cognitively. The consequences of poor nutrition include poor behaviour, increased body fat, slower mental processes, less alert, and slower muscle response. Poor diet can damage intelligence.

Insufficient consumption of protein and micro-nutrients (minerals and vitamins) leads to malnutrition. The effects of malnutrition include failure to grow, poor concentration, low self esteem, and fatigue, which can effect outcomes in other areas, especially learning. Signs of malnutrition include being unusually irritable, sluggish or anxious.

There are links between food deficiencies and mental health problems in young people. It is thought that one in five children may well have a diagnosable mental health problem.

Benefits of good nutrition

Childhood is recognised as the critical time for healthy growth and the basis for future attainment of every child. The benefits of good nutrition include proper growth and development, increased energy, bone and muscle strength, healthy brain and concentration, and weight control, leading to reduced risk of diabetes, obesity, and chronic diseases. Good nutrition is the basis to learn good habits for life.

The benefits of supplements

Studies have shown that vitamins, minerals and oils have proven benefits. Vitamin supplements significantly improve behaviour of juvenile delinquents, as well as improving their IQ, and vitamins increase non-verbal IQ. Essential fats improve behaviour, especially with ADHD children.

How it works

Philippa our nutritionist explains: 'Before the initial session, parents are asked to complete a questionnaire to provide relevant information including medical history, current medication, if any, and a record of what food and drink the child has consumed during the previous four days.

The questionnaire also gathers details of the presenting problem, its duration, what treatment had been sought, any behavioural difficulties and parents' coping strategies.

A child's medical history is important, illness and infections, past and present. Past issues help determine the present state of the immune system, and the burden that some medication may have put on their bodies.

It is useful to know what has been said about the condition by conventional health professionals and what the children and parents feel about that. Having tried other complementary assistance may indicate open-mindedness to new ideas, but if it was found not to have worked adequately, the family may be dubious about Clover House therapy being successful. This must be addressed speedily if lasting results are to be achieved.

Education

Nutritional help is essentially about education. It offers practical information and teaches people how they can gradually incorporate new ideas into their existing dietary habits. Help is given over three or more sessions, and monitored via client scores, verbal and documented, with handouts given to clients, and in my own consultation notes.

Learning from adults

At Clover House we are of course focusing on children. Experience has shown that they learn far more from the examples of adults than from being told what to do. Sometimes parents will explain that the child 'won't eat vegetables' then reveal that they 'only like carrots' themselves. If permanent improvement is to be achieved, the parents are included as well.

Advice on current diet

From the questionnaire I will explain how the food you eat or don't eat may be contributing to how you feel and that changing your diet could help significantly. Other advice might include eating more of certain kinds of foods, or eating at certain times of the day, which foods to avoid, and what to drink.

Hobbies and Sports

I look at hobbies and sports, whether they are physical or sociable, and explain how nutrition can help improve their sporting ability. This makes it more interesting and motivates children to try the suggested dietary changes. Rapport is enhanced by encouraging them to talk about their interests and how they get on with their friends, giving valuable clues about their character.

Involving children

To gain the child's co-operation it is important to include them, even if quite young, in discussions with parents. It is usually the mother who prepares the family's food and it is she who will be encouraging the child to follow recommendations. Some parents become very defensive, feeling they are being criticised for the child's former eating habits, which they are being asked to change. This can be a handicap to progress, and needs to be dealt with promptly if a good rapport is to be established.

I encourage the parents to buy and cook new foods for the family and change the way they eat. Even sitting down to have a meal together may be difficult if they have rarely done so. It is vital that children and parents are brought into the discussion so that the suggested measures are accepted by everyone concerned.

Focusing on food
Sugar – the main issue

Many people do not control their blood-sugar levels.

From childhood we are drawn to sweet things, and parents commonly use them to reward or express affection towards their offspring.

There are common misconceptions about the amount of sugar a child consumes. It is often disguised in processed food; there is sugar in fruit and fruit juices, and that effects children too. I generally give a detailed explanation of the peaks and troughs caused by too much sugar in the diet.

Breakfast

It comes as a surprise to many to discover that cornflakes and a glass of fruit juice do not constitute a healthy breakfast. Porridge oats are healthy – but the process of making them into other oat products can turn a good carbohydrate into a simple carbohydrate which can affect blood sugar levels.

Is there a routine? What food (if any!) is eaten. Is the atmosphere calm or rushed? Breakfast is commonly regarded as the most important meal of the day. I ask additional questions so that I can get a picture of the morning routine. Similarly, enquiring about other meals at home or school can provide valuable information.

Protein

I talk about the different protein foods you can eat, as most people think protein is just a lump of meat. An example is how parents can include nuts and seeds at breakfast, or introduce them into the rest of the day.

Generally I advocate protein at every meal and snack by explaining how this holds the food in the stomach and allows smaller amounts at a time into the digestive system to be digested so they get a steady release of glucose into

Let food be your medicine and medicine thy food. Hippocrates

The part can never be well unless the whole is well. Plato

Today more than 95% of all chronic disease is caused by food choice, toxic food ingredients, nutritional deficiencies and lack of physical exercise. Mike Adams

The food you eat can be either the safest and most powerful form of medicine or the slowest form of poison. Ann Wigmore

You can become just as hooked on sugar as on drugs, tobacco or alcohol. The sugar affects the same areas in your brain. Thorbjorg Hafestensdottir

Only bacteria thrive and live well in a poorly cared for body. Nina Leavins

We are all warned to read labels. The salutary truth is we shouldn't be eating anything that has a label on it.
T C Fry

Your health is what you make of it. Everything you do and think either adds to the vitality, energy and spirit you possess, or takes away from it.
Ann Wignmore

I believe parents need to make nutrition education a priority in their homes. It is crucial for good health and longevity to instil in your children sound eating habits from an early age. Cat Cora

their bloodstream. I explain that they become much more stable in both their energy levels and mentally because of the slow release of energy throughout the day.

Snacks

I explain how important it is to have three meals and two to three snacks a day. I reassure the young girls that this is not going to put on weight, it is going to give energy for what they want to do.

Also parents forget that children as young as 8 may be entering puberty, which can make them moody, aggressive and hungry.

Oily fish

Oily fish is recommended several times a week. Often children say they hate it, and I suggest if they like mashed potato or bubble and squeak, then put a bit of tinned salmon in and fry it as fishcakes. Get the children to do it for fun, and gradually over the weeks introduce more salmon.

Hydration

Allowing your body to become dehydrated can produce many symptoms including irritability, fatigue, hunger, loss of concentration and memory, headaches, and weight gain. I stress to children and parents that what they drink is as important as how much.

Most parents know that fizzy drinks are bad, but many believe that drinking fruit juice all day is good for them. I explain how these are overly high in sugar too, even though the sugar they contain is a natural sugar. If children are reluctant to drink more water, I suggest diluting fruit juice 50:50 to reduce sugar content.

Conflicting influences

Sometimes divorced or separated parents send conflicting messages to their child about what foods are acceptable. There might be an unconscious attempt by one parent to undermine the other. Grandparents too have been known to ignore professional advice and give the child too many unhealthy treats.

Apart from the psychological issue of divided loyalties, this discourages the child from accepting and trying out new dietary habits, and reinforces the likelihood of rebellion against the parent trying to instil a healthy regime.

Guided by the Clover House nutritionist, difficulties of this kind are addressed and, where possible, the whole family is involved in making improvements.

Increasing the range of foods

Some children have a surprisingly restricted number of foods that they are willing to eat – perhaps as few as five or six – which can require considerable patience and ingenuity if permanent change is to be achieved. As a rule, it is important that children take part in preparing their food because it gives them a sense of 'ownership' which is absent when, for example, merely opening a packet of crisps.

Introducing a child to new tastes usually requires sensitivity and coaxing. Explaining the potential benefits of new foods can help, and that new-tasting food may need as many as fifteen trials before it is accepted.

Parental support and encouragement are important, although it can be very disheartening to a mother when, instead of heating up the customary microwaved meal, she cooks healthier food and the child refuses to eat it. This challenge can often be remedied by inviting the child to have fun by joining in with the cooking – eating it afterwards then becomes a must!

Other advice might include eating more of certain kinds of foods, or eating at certain times of the day, which foods to avoid and which drinks are OK.

Home prepared foods

I always emphasise the benefits of home-prepared food and therefore the absence of any (harmful) additives. Not everything with an E number is harmful, e.g. Vitamin C.

Where to eat

Meals should take a minimum of twenty minute to eat, and I suggest making a small ceremony or occasion of it. It's a nice time to have a good chat with everybody in the family, enjoy that time together, and to eat more slowly. Often children eat quickly. To sit down calmly, without TV or screens, helps digestion.

Supplements

No bad diet can be made good just by introducing supplements. Good food is the best option, but sometimes supplements are needed to provide the extra components needed to restore optimum health. There are no general rules; however a good multivitamin and mineral can be helpful if children are fussy eaters, or have extra stress such as illness, sports, exams or school pressures.

Children with digestive problems may benefit from having a probiotic to help restore the correct balance of gut flora. Fish oil supplements may often be a useful addition, especially if they dislike oily fish.

Handouts

Suggestions and information are given out in special handouts such as understanding blood sugar levels, how to introduce vegetables into a child's diet, or advice on certain conditions such as asthma and eczema, etc.

Some mothers' experiences of nutrition:

'We had a real problem because her diet wasn't good. Most of the things she ate were sugar-based. Basically we had to completely cut out most of the diet she was on and gradually introduce new things, i.e. she wasn't allowed squash or fizzy drinks, nor processed ham, she had to have fresh ham.'

'She was moody but it gradually turned around. She is so much happier and it's not really an issue now. We just plod along and try doing a bit at a time. I've actually bought a book about labels and additives, and it tells you how to read labels properly. We had been eating this stuff for years. Awful. It was fascinating reading labels and finding out what's in foods and the damage that can be done. Incredible really.'

'I didn't realise how much it could affect a child, things like jam sandwiches, I mean I'm not being funny, that's a natural thing to give children, but you don't realise that it's not good for them because of the amount of sugar. I won't touch white bread now, I have brown and oatmeal bread. We are all healthier and we have all lost weight.'

'We were advised to cut out all dairy produce, squashes and fizzy drinks and as many foods as possible containing preservatives – that meant me learning to cook. I did with a vengeance – now in the cupboards is goat's milk and organic produce like I can't imagine! We learnt valuable information that will help my son make informed choices about healthy living for the rest of his life, as well as how to tailor his diet in times of stress to lesson the symptoms.'

'It was quite a dramatic change in his diet really, because although we thought we were giving him a healthy diet, we didn't realise that we were giving him quite a lot that wasn't helpful. I think the diet made the most difference, within days he was a different boy. He actually liked the vegetables and fruit, he took to it really well. And cutting out sugar, he seemed to understand that it was helping him feel better, and he started drinking lots of water. We were so glad to be able to do something practical to help him.'

'We are making flapjacks which were lovely, the only problem was everybody loved them.'

'We cut out additives and fizzy drinks and things like that, and in general he was calmer and he seemed a lot happier, and he was willing to try the new foods, because it was explained to him. We are all eating the same things now.'

'It was a little bit difficult, but as it was for Amanda's benefit, any help at that time, I made sure I was going to follow through. You have to change the way you shop basically, because you're programmed to go into the supermarket with your list of tins of this and that. We do prepare things now, and we don't buy a lot of processed foods, but it's just different ingredients really. There were some things we were recommended to eat more of, and some less, and it's easy to just follow the instructions.'

'It's not a huge change, to be honest, and I think if I can do it and work full time, anyone can do it. One thing we do is cook some meat, put all the vegetables in one pan and simmer them, make some gravy and it takes about twenty minutes. You just have to think ahead to make sure you've got some fresh food in really.'

A child's experience of nutrition:
'I'm upset 'cos I can't have the nice sweets that I see – 'cos it makes me angry and go doolally.'

Nutritional help for Alan and Tim with Learning Difficulties
'When Alan was 4 and Tim 3, we were given a diagnosis – Landau Kleffner Syndrome covered all of their symptoms which had become apparent from about 18 months of age in each of them. There was loss of expressive and receptive language, dyspraxia, autistic tendencies, attention deficit disorder and attention deficit hyperactive disorder.

We thought now we had a diagnosis, we could start treatment and things would get better for us. How wrong we were! The seizures started a couple of months later, when we had anti-epileptic drugs. When they didn't work they had courses of high-dose steroids. Steroids gave us glimpses of normality, but generally everything spiralled out of control. As they lost even more skills there was an inevitable increase in doctor's visits, increased medication, but no answers as to why they were just getting worse other than that their condition is one of regression and advancement.

No-one knew how many regressions they would have. Tim did not appear to get many side effects from the medication, but Alan got them all. He gained 25 kg in three years. We even lost sight of their previous 'normal intelligence.''

The practical implications of managing the boys became impossible. Neither of them could be educated or socialised in a mainstream school, so they were transferred to a special school. Alan went to a school for complex learning difficulties and Tim for severe learning difficulties.

After hearing a talk by Paul Shattock on autism and diet, we started the boys on a gluten- and dairy-free diet. We were bothered about vitamins and minerals so asked for a dietician. We were not willing to wait four months for the NHS as we had already started the diet, when someone told us about Clover House.

We did not have to wait to be seen and we were greeted with open arms. We were not treated as a series of symptoms anymore, but as individuals within a family unit with varying needs. As a consequence we all received therapy. Although it was very difficult at times, the discussions, practical techniques, dietary and supplementary information enabled us to take control of our health, treatment and therefore, our futures.

Within three months we saw a stabilisation of the boys' medical condition to the extent we were able to reduce drug dosages. The continued improvements in their seizures, educational ability, happiness and wellbeing spurred us on until they became medication-free. Less than two years later they remain both drug and seizure free.

The gains they made continue to snowball and health and educational professionals agree with our observations with good and positive reports, although still cannot offer an explanation for the complete change.

These changes have presented us with different but still difficult decisions to make. The highs and lows we have felt during this time have been difficult, but everyone at Clover

House has been very supportive throughout. They have helped us realise which way to turn in a rapidly changing situation.

Having already come a long way we do not know how far the future will take us, but are very thankful for the love, support, help and advice that has been available as and when we needed it.'

Mum, a nurse, subsequently re-trained as a nutritionist.

Chapter 4

Why Massage?

Of all the senses, touch is the first to develop. The experience of massage is said to begin at birth, as the muscles deliver the baby through the birth canal by rhythmic contractions. After we are born we experience holding, rocking, washing and caressing.

As we become more independent our hands can squeeze and scratch and soothe our discomfort. The body massages itself when breathing from the diaphragm muscles, and movement of limbs keeps the circulation flowing, arms swinging naturally by our sides as we walk, relaxing the back muscles.

Vital for life

Research has shown that baby monkeys deprived of touch will die. The language of touch tells us we are not alone, it gives reassurance, warmth, pleasure, comfort and renewed vitality.

Touch is instinctive. 'Let's rub it better', our natural response to children's bumps and bruises; hands soothe headaches. Emotional pain evokes holding, comforting, hugging, stroking to convey sympathy, understanding and reassurance.

Studies

Other studies show that massaging premature babies led to increased weight gain and a shorter stay in hospital. Asthmatic children can breathe more easily with fewer attacks; teenagers with anorexia and depression reported better body image, improved self esteem and less depression.

Benefits – To the Body

Massage improves circulation and skin condition, stimulates growth, and offers passive exercise reducing atrophy of muscles, eases aches and pains, and increases flexibility and function of muscles and joints.

Massage supports respiration and deeper breathing patterns. It improves the immune system by increasing lymph flow, and reduces cortisol (stress hormone).

Benefits – For the Emotions and the Mind

Massage and appropriate touch helps children relax and learn to calm themselves and better able to manage stress. It helps relieve anxiety and depression. Psychological effects include reducing shock, fear, tension, increased sense of wellbeing, self-awareness and self-acceptance.

It supports and increases thinking and verbal skills.

Benefits – Socially

Touch can convey a thousand words, and children are known to thrive with the right amount of physical touch.

Massage can increase speech and language skills and help to build trust, friendship and respect.

Children with healthy views of touch are known to grow up into adults with good self esteem and to develop long-standing relationships. It helps them grow into a balanced and mature adult. Healthy touch is essential to producing a healthy child.

Violence

Dr James Prescott, a former member of the National Institute of Child Health and Human Development has concluded that the presence or absence of touch, as well as cultural practices regarding touch, are the two most important factors that differentiate violent or non-violent cultures.

He states, 'The principal cause of human violence is a lack of bodily pleasure derived from touching and stroking during the formative years.'

Helps bonding

Most importantly, massage between a parent and child increases bonding and allows children to feel loved, and relaxes and calms the giver and receiver.

Parents benefit from having time out, to focus on one good thing, and forget day to day concerns. It can also be a special time for one to one talking and sharing, enabling children to share their worries and concerns.

Appropriate for any age

From premature infants, babies, infants, toddlers, pre-schoolers, growing children and adolescents benefit from massage and positive touch. By connecting a child back to their parent in a non-threatening environment (fully dressed and in a quiet, safe, warm room) the child is able to enjoy the benefits of physical relaxation and touch.

Various techniques

A variety of techniques can be used from squidging and rocking muscles to holding, pressure positions of shiatsu, flowing effleurage (a light, skimming touch), stroking, rubbing, gentle pressure, gliding, feathering, stretching, kneading muscles, mobilising joints, reflexology points on the feet and hands, to the metamorphic technique of stroking and tapping.

Practical demonstration and experience

Using a massage couch, we give practical demonstrations showing how to use the body for flow of energy, rather than using the force of hands, arms or back. We emphasise that a slow pace is essential for the body to trust and relax.

Altered state

With slow pace and care, the parent can usually see and experience their child relaxing into an altered state, the day dreaming, hypnogogic state that aids healing. With a few good massages the child is conditioned to relax, day dream, or fall asleep – parents often report that their child fell asleep within ten minutes.

Length of time

From a few minutes, thirty minutes to one hour, depending on the age of the child and the child's willingness. By sharing these techniques parents are empowered to continue to use it at any time, at times of stress and anxiety, or as a routine before bed to aid sleep. It's a good time especially for boisterous boys, and an alternative for addictive computer games and television.

Additional time in sessions

During sessions, parents and children also have the opportunity to meet other therapists, to tell their story, discuss, and gain more helpful information and advice.

Flower Remedies

An information sheet listing and briefly explaining the thirty-three Bach flower remedies is given to the parents or child or who can then 'diagnose' their feelings and fears, and a mixture of up to seven remedies is made up.

If there is time, it's a great way of involving children in their own 'magic' prescription which they can do themselves and take separately or in drinks throughout the week.

Our Massage therapist Kym says,

'At Clover House I give the child a short massage and then show the parents a simple massage routine they can use at home. I help to build their confidence by giving lots of encouragement, and stressing the importance of enjoying the time spent together.

When a child is causing problems at home with difficult behaviour or being unhappy, it can bring out feelings of guilt in parents and this can affect their feelings for their child. Massage is a non-verbal way of strengthening and reinforcing their bond with the child, and is something that all parents know how to do, once they have been shown a few simple techniques.

I encourage the whole family to get involved. Often when there is a 'difficult' child in a family, the other children can miss out on a parent's attention. Grand-parents, siblings, mums and dads, can all benefit from this great therapy.

In today's world with frequent family break ups, working parents, school pressures, and the general pace of life, there is a greater need than ever for parents to find a way of connecting with their children.'

Cala Jo, another of our massage therapists explains,

'I like to create a relaxing and welcoming atmosphere so both parent and child are able to engage fully in the massage session. I start by talking you through the benefits of massage and relate how this can help with your present experience. If appropriate I may also talk a little about breathing and how when we breathe in a certain way this can help us to feel calmer in challenging situations.

If your child is willing, we start on the massage couch fully clothed, and I talk you through some simple massage techniques. This is very much an interactive, hands on and fun session; the child usually enjoys both of us working on them at the same time! There is lots of time for any questions and you are given a booklet and massage information sheet which you can use for reference at home.

If the child is a bit apprehensive then we start by doing a simple hand or foot massage while the child sits in the chair. Rapport is built over the weeks and the child usually begins to feel more and more comfortable so is then happy to move onto the couch.

You are asked to practise the massage with your child for 5–20 minutes several days a week or even every day if possible.

During the second session we talk about how the massage has helped, and I will go through the routine again with you and answer any questions that have arisen during the week.

During the third session and other follow ups we talk through your progress and other tips and advice may be given. Questions do arise and there is time for this too.

Often in these sessions there's more space for your child to receive a massage for 20–25 minutes. This allows your child to begin to relax deeply and often parents comment how calm they feel just being in the room and watching it happen.'

Relaxation tape and handouts

A relaxation tape for children might be given, as well as handouts showing the body techniques, and massage oil for use at home.

Some mothers' experiences of massage

'From day one he started sleeping through the night, you know it was a real dramatic change with the sleeping, and he was less irritable almost straight away as a result of – I think feeling better in himself. '

'They weren't interested in the fact that he was irritable and not sleeping, and it was affecting his day to day life – I was getting depressed through lack of sleep, my husband used to dread coming home, we were not getting quality time together. My health visitor tried to help, but she had the same basic medical approach – I mean we tried the so-called controlled crying techniques at night time, but it wasn't that he was waking in the night for attention.

After visiting Clover House Alex would have a massage after his bath before going to bed, and he'd start falling asleep while he was having it, and from day one really he started sleeping through the night, every night – that was a dramatic change.'

'I didn't really think it would help, but I think it was just the bonding and the contact – doing something – you know, you do the general things when you're a busy Mum – you don't think hands on. We do lots of cuddles, but the massage was really good at the end of the day. It was just easy, it's not difficult at all. I would definitely advise anyone to get their hands on their children.'

'The massage was especially fun because you can have one whenever you want and it's good for both of us to relax. You can both spend time together so that's better, and it only takes a few minutes. We tend to do it now if Amy's got any worries, and have a chat and then she goes straight to sleep.'

'I don't think anyone would find it difficult because there's no right or wrong way. I think once you've got the oils on your hands and you start to move it around, it's just the physical contact that's the most important.

We were shown some techniques, try this and try that, and we would have a go. I do my daughter's back and shoulders because she gets tension, and we do feet and ankles every night. To be honest a lot of it is having contact, you are close and touching, while you are talking and we have chats, and it just helps.'

One Mum burst into tears after seeing her son 'looking different and so relaxed. Just what he needs,' she said. After years of back pain with rods in his back, her son had a fear and phobia of constant hospital appointments and surgery. She just wished she had realised that she could have helped him throughout that time.

'I experienced the wonderful satisfaction of empowerment. I as a mother have been able to help my child with just my intuition, heart, head and hands.'

*'Life takes it out of you,
but massage puts it back.'*

Clare Maxwell Hudson, Therapist,
author and teacher of Massage.

*'Massage is food
for the heart.'*

Kirsten Norman, writer.

*'Massage is an energy
medicine with great
preventative power.'*

Linda Robson, writer.

*'As you think,
so shall you be.'*

Hippocrates, the father of medicine,
advocated massage with oils.

Children's comments on massage:
'Is this it? Can I come back tomorrow?'

'Mummy didn't have time to do any massage, so I did it myself.'

'I like Clover House because it's helping me with my feelings, and making me feel much happier. We talk about what our family eats and then my favourite – the massage. After the massage my brain tells me to say out loud – I want to go to sleep.'

'I gave Dad a massage – and he fell asleep, and me and my brother stayed up late watching the television!'

Quotes on Massage
With 30 years experience in massage, and degrees in Education and Special Education, Peggy J. Farlow states,
'By teaching a care-giver or family how to successfully offer nurturing touch and massage to their child (especially a special needs child), I believe we begin to heal the world.'

Joan Boorysenko, Co-founder and director of Mind/Body Clinic, Harvard Medical School says:
'Stress-related disorders make up 80–90% of ailments that bring people to family practice physicians. What they require is someone to listen, someone to touch them, someone to care. That does not exist in modern medicine.
Touch is most absent in the healing process. Years ago massage was a big part of nursing. There was so much care, so much touch, so much goodness conveyed through massage. Now nurses for the most part are as busy as

physicians. They are writing charts, doing procedures and notes, with no time for massage any more. People are afraid of being sued if they touch. A teacher can't even touch a crying child any more. What has happened in our society regarding touch is truly pathetic.

Massage therapy is absolutely key in the healing process, not only because it relieves stress, it is foundational in the healing process any time and anywhere.'

Massage is Medicine

Massage has been an essential part of all aspects of traditional medicine for thousands of years in India, China, Japan, Thailand, Ancient Greece and Rome.

Massage communicates right into the heart of a person in a language more powerful than the spoken word, and yet is immediately understood.

'The first and most important thing is that it works,' says Dr Deepak Chopra, Head of Health Centre in America, employing 15 massage therapists. 'What I love about massage is that it's so simple. You've got everything you need, literally at your fingertips.'

'Every child, no matter what age, should be massaged at bedtime on a regular basis.' Tiffany Field, PhD., Touch Research Institute in Miami USA.

'Touch is essential to a child's development, sense of wellbeing and good health. Children reach out for touch as naturally as they do for food and water. A nightly massage can ensure that touch is a positive, nurturing part of their human experience, and as Field says, 'They love it'.'

Chapter 5

Why Imagery?

Dr Maxwell Maltz was one of the first to realise the way the brain works (confirmed by studies), that it cannot differentiate between real and synthetic, vividly imagined experiences. i.e. Your brain cannot tell the difference between real memories and vividly imagined 'memories'.

Given that you can train your brain to visualise anything you desire, if you visualise what you want, your subconscious will believe that you have already achieved it – and give you the resources you need to succeed.

Placebo effect

It is recognised that the placebo effect works, a beneficial effect that cannot be attributed to the properties of the placebo itself, and therefore must be due to the patient's belief in that 'treatment'. A sugar pill and even fake surgery have been shown to work. Some studies attribute this to meaning, optimism or expectation. Even a plaster or bandage with a cartoon on it heals a child's wound faster than a plaster without.

Mind-Body connection

Dr Candace Pert scientifically proved that all cells have memories and communicate via neuropeptides. Moods and mental states are not just in the mind, but in the body and organs as well. Thoughts, emotions, and beliefs are not just subjective ideas in the mind, but cause real chemical and physical changes in the brain and throughout the body.

Neuro Linguistic Programming – NLP

The majority of techniques used in our Imagery Therapy are from Neuro Linguistic Programming or NLP. NLP has been defined as the art of personal development, and provides the possibility of modifying the most complicated mental states with simple techniques.

'Neuro' refers to the fact that all our behaviour stems from our neurological processes such as what we see, feel, hear, smell and taste.

'Linguistic' is because we use language to order our thoughts and behaviour, and to communicate with others. We also use non-spoken language to communicate, e.g. body language and posture.

'Programming' references the fact we can enter new programs into our brain, e.g. new ways of thinking or acting, new habits and beliefs. If you are capable of learning a new skill, you can succeed with NLP. For example, if you can tie your shoelaces, you can learn new skills.

You use your brain and your senses to see what's going on (neuro). You adjust your methods of talking and communicating to get useful results (linguistic), and you change the way you think and act to achieve your goals (programming).

Sports psychology and coaching has successfully used these techniques for many years. In experiments with three groups: One – doing nothing. Two – practising the sport, and Three – *imagining* doing the sport better – the group that improved the most was the one that used their imagination.

Two Problems

John, our imagery therapist, used to say there are only two problems – either a habit or an emotion – and both can be sorted out.

A Habit

We all learn from childhood that repetition creates a habit. Thoughts and actions correspond to a neuro pathway in the brain, and the more we repeat a thought or action, the stronger the habit becomes. Habits are in everything we do from gestures, how we talk, what we eat, what we think and what we feel. A habit is like a river of energy, and energy never disappears. To change a habit it needs to be caught early and, like a stream of water, you can divert its course.

The most famous example of learning a habit was in the late 1900s when a Russian scientist called Pavlov conducted experiments of offering food to dogs when ringing a bell. After several times the dogs associated the bell with food, and in a short time, when the bell was rung without food, the dogs would salivate. With repetition a neurological connection had been created in the mind of the dogs.

The brain has millions of neurological pathways and when we do something new, a pathway is made in order to re-access the experience more easily. The more we repeat a behaviour, we strengthen the neuro pathway, and research shows that these pathways get larger by repetition and this is how we get 'hard-wired'. So we can re-wire our pathways with new and positive re-enforcement.

An Emotion

If you asked a child to increase their heartbeat, it probably would not work, but if that child were to vividly imagine a monster in the dark, getting closer and closer – their heartbeat would most likely quicken.

This is because the key programmes of human behaviour are habit and imagination, and they are far more powerful than logic and willpower.

Human behaviour is also the result of 'state' or 'mood'. The pictures and sounds in our minds, and how we make them = our state = our physiology (posture, tension breathing, etc.) = behaviour.

Visualisation

Anybody can visualise. An example used is – what does your front door look like, what is the colour, where is the handle? To answer this you used your imagination and made pictures in your mind. Children can do this better than adults, they still believe in Father Christmas and magic.

Most people operate from negative images and visualisation, making their own horror movies. By learning to change the pictures and sounds in your mind you can make more useful movies.

A memory can be 'viewed' from the inside or the outside. Inside, the memory intensifies the feeling. Outside, the memory reduces the intensity of the feelings. So you can diminish an unpleasant or stressful experience by stepping outside and making it smaller and dimmer or further away.

You can intensify a positive or resourceful experience by stepping inside the image and making it brighter and bigger.

Some Imagery Techniques explained

One of the first imagery examples used is called 'Special Place'. When a child goes to bed, instead of thinking about the monsters under the bed, they are asked to think of their best special place. Typically girls imagine being in a Disney- land Castle, and boys scoring goals for Manchester United!

A 'special secret garden' can be used, with all the good things they want in it. We have had children imagining playing with the friends they lost after moving to a different school, and therefore did not 'miss' them so much. Blowing a 'sleep flower' with suggestions that it will help them sleep. Hyperactive, boisterous boys actually get rid of excess energy by imagining playing in the playground, jumping on the trampoline, etc.

Imagery is also used to clear physical complaints or pain with techniques such as being asked what is its size, what is the colour, what does it want, and perhaps change it to smaller, or move it away, change it to their favourite colour.

Another imagery technique is to ask what their condition means to the child, examples being asthma – like an elephant on the chest, or an elastic band round the chest, and the therapist allows the child to describe their own interpretation and visualisation, and follows the scenario to a positive conclusion. The symptoms, pains, etc can often be alleviated in this way.

There is a variety of techniques showing how we use imagery and how we use NLP in the case studies. John our therapist also produced his own techniques for children in the majority of the case studies, (explained by two children later).

How it works

An NLP therapist has been trained to get rapport, so that

a child will enjoy his time with them, and feel connected, heard, want to do some 'mind' work, and come back! In fact sometimes a child will experience for the first time an adult talking at his own level, speaking with the same language, tone, inflection, etc, mirroring his actions, and will automatically communicate back.

According to how a child comes across (some haven't been able to look at an adult or talk to an adult) and what the problems or conditions are, the therapist uses various techniques he thinks appropriate.

By using pictures in the mind, work can be done without lots of talking, without discussing any upset, just by asking a child to think about the problem. In half an hour or so perhaps several 'interventions' can be achieved, including some with a parent if necessary, and these techniques can be tested to see if they have worked. There is also the opportunity of two further sessions to do more intervention work. The skill is in choosing the technique, its delivery and teaching.

Some children's comments about their imagery experience with John.

Amy age 10 who came for food issues, panic attacks and her parents' separation, used the car wash technique:

'We didn't know quite what to make of John. I hadn't heard of imagery before, and didn't really know what to expect at all. The thing I remembered most was the car wash.

'My dad's wife is not very nice and she was being mean. I was asked to take all the meanness out of her and what you do in your mind, you know when you go through a car wash. I had to go into it and make her stand on this circle and hose her down – you open their belly button and you stick the hose in it and wash all the mean stuff out, and you spray them with rainbow colours.

When I meet people now I think car wash in my head, and do it to them. How about that!'

Another child preferred the Babushka doll technique:

'There were these Russian dolls, that all fit inside one another. On one of them she didn't look very happy, so John laid them all out on the table and he said, 'Well, when she was younger she wasn't happy at all.' He went to the next biggest one and said she's not as unhappy as before, because she's got some friends, and then went to the next one and said she's got more friends and you can see a smile on her face. I think John was trying to tell us that throughout your life you get happy times and you get sad times, and if you think back, maybe not so long ago, you could find a place that was happy, then something bad might happen, but then something good happens and you feel happy again. So think about the times in your life when you were happy, and then forget about the bad stuff.'

A mother's comments on imagery with her three-year-old daughter who had post traumatic stress from a car accident and a fear of men and cars:

'I don't really know what he did, it was more play because she was so frightened of him when we walked into the room, and she hid and she just sat next to me shivering. He basically ignored her and curiosity, I suppose, got the better of her, and gradually she would come out and he would play games with her – magic tricks, just different things to get her confidence. He came right down to her level and did things with her.

Paracelsus, one of the leading physicians of the Rennaissance, said

'The imagination has the power to cause and cure illness.'

Hippocrates agreed with him. 'As you think so shall you be.'

'When someone's attitude changes, the world can become a completely different place for them.'

Gemma Baily, NLP therapist.

'The human mind is like an umbrella – it functions best when open.'

Walter Gropius

It's hard to explain but whatever he did, it worked because within weeks she was a different child completely. We carried on the techniques at home, things he showed us. He told us to be positive with her.

We were going on holiday so it was suggested we take the monster with us and not to forget to leave the monster on holiday, which we did and it actually worked. That's how we got rid of the monster.'

George's mother brought him along because of poor development and constipation.

'George was only 4 and was very poorly, including constipation, and the imagery therapist picked up the negative points, and discussed the positive points, and sort of gave George the option to choose a more positive way. We weren't sure that he would understand because he has developmental delay, and in the sessions it didn't seem like it was working, but when we came home it was apparent that he had picked up the message.'

'It was a really lovely experience, we were giggling half the time. Some of the things were quite natural, and you think, why didn't I think of that? It was a natural thing to say to your child, but you are so pent up and anxious about getting it right, that it doesn't come to you. We still refer to it now.'

'We found it a godsend, we needed the advice that John gave. I think the main thing we got from it is somebody understanding what we were going through, and saying this is not a naughty child.'

Fiona's mother brought her along with glue ear and behaviour problems.

'He made the both of us feel at ease and allowed us to get used to the surroundings and the toys, and my young daughter felt comfortable around him. John focused more on me and I knew why deep down. If I'd been discussing this a year ago, I would have been reduced to tears and very frightened, but since working with John I can write the following without the fear that has plagued me since a child.

I had been bullied since the age of 5 until the age of 13, mentally and physically. I have had counselling in the past and was put on antidepressants, but this opened up old wounds which could not be healed and prevented me from enjoying life to the full.

His approach enables you to turn negative thoughts, feelings and behaviour into positive reactions to situations without even having to dig up bad memories. I went away with coping strategies and could not remember the first time I was bullied which was wonderful and cathartic.

NLP is nothing to fear, all it does is give you some control over how you deal with difficult situations that can frighten you and prevent you from getting on with life.

So although I came for my daughter, I realised that her behaviour was half diet and half emotional as she clearly reacted to my feelings when I was down, and seemed to know instinctively that I found it very difficult to be tactile due to my past. Since working with John I have become more open with my daughter and she comes to me for cuddles knowing I am genuinely reciprocating her feelings.'

Some children's comments about Imagery
'John helped me think about what I'd done and what I

can do better, and what had happened to him that had made him choose what to do. He was really nice about that. He made me smile a lot, and just talked to me and made me think about all the things I could have done instead.'

'I felt really angry inside, and I would express my anger in an aggressive way. I don't feel that way now, and if I feel angry I would shed it, and make it smaller and explain it to my family, but not in an aggressive way, just talking about it.'

In a talk to parents John explained: 'Imagery has five aspects: what it looks like, what it sounds like, what it feels like, what it smells like and what it tastes like, and the three most important are what it looks like, what it sounds like and what it feels like. It's individual.

If you are looking at the world and you think about it you get an image of it, and whatever you are noticing – that is your world, and you are living in it. If somebody else is looking at it they are not seeing that at all.'

John shows a toy and explains, 'My wife came home from work upset because she had opened a broken chocolate egg with a toy inside, and was saying look at this little man. Others at work had said it was a bird, and when I said it was a bird she started crying, and accused me of being in league with those at work telling her it was a bird. In the end I tried holding it exactly as my wife had done and it was an old man, but now my wife saw a little bird. Once you are used to seeing one of them it's hard to see that it is also something else.

Actually there is a third way of looking at this – it's a toy numbered KA8N107, which you would need to know in an auction because you can collect them. It's also a piece of extruded plastic with paint on it, so there are at least four ways of looking at it.

'Brains aren't designed to get results; they go in directions. If you know how the brain works you can set your own directions. If you don't, then someone else will.'
Richard Bandler, NLP trainer.

'We all make maps in our brain to make sense of life and communicate. NLP teaches children to change their maps so they can gain confidence, or motivation, or overcome fears, manage emotions, develop self resilience, learn new ways of thinking to help their inner potential to shine.'
Karen Beveridge, Kids NLP Scotland

'Its simplicity allows even the youngest of children to participate, believing that they are simply using their imaginations.'
Penni Mead, NLP Therapist.

Everybody has a different way of experiencing reality. There is no such thing as reality because everybody has their own experience of it, and imagery is about getting a better one. If you are a child in trouble, and you are looking at the world you are living in and feeling it and sensing it in every way, and it doesn't work, well maybe one way out is to experience it differently, and imagery is said to be about finding a more useful way of experiencing the world you are living in.

The Problem is separate to the child

'We deal with children,' continues John, 'and they all come in families of some kind and we help children, and their parents, their brothers and sisters. So a child comes here with a problem. The way we see it is, here is a child, beautifully designed and works perfectly, and here is their problem floating around bothering them because they don't know how to deal with it.

So you haven't got a problem child, you have a child and you have a problem. Problems can be solved. Another way of looking at it is that you help a parent or a child see that problem in a different light and find a way through it. There are lots of techniques you can use.'

Confidence

Children come here with a problem and if they have had the problem for sometime, I bet you anything they have started to lose confidence in themselves – it seems to go together. So one of the things we do in imagery is show them how they can help themselves. I can't help anybody – all I can do is create space and a few hints and let them make the changes themselves. Parents can do this too.

'Calm contemplative environment and non-invasive approach to healing'

'How warm and friendly everyone made us feel'

'That a group of people were willing to listen to my concerns. That it was drug free.'

'Finding someone who understood our problems – and such quick results.'

'I liked the fact that the whole person is dealt with, from diet to relaxation to talking about your problems.'

Working with Mum

'I often work with Mum,' continues John, 'because if I can get Mum to see the problem differently, suddenly the child is seeing it differently, and it disappears and everyone is happy. So you don't have to work with the person who has the problem. You can work with someone else.'

Watching self in the third person

There are many ways of seeing things differently… so if you are thinking about going to school and you imagine yourself when it wasn't working for you – you get all of those bad feelings. But if you try it a different way and think, 'When I go to school tomorrow I will be …' and watch someone who looks like you but is a day older, arriving and doing things and doing them reasonably well, there's no emotion attached to it, apart from, 'Oh I seem to be doing that OK.'

So getting a third person (outside) view of the situation can often be better than doing the first person view – the technique version of what you think about tomorrow, if you *see* yourself there doing better, it works.

If you imagine yourself there it's pretty frightening. If an exam is coming up and you are imagining yourself there … you can't read the paper and you fail and you get upset. But if you see yourself differently, being there with everyone else, writing away, you will feel more confident about passing that exam. Perception is a big way of changing things.

Patterns established

We often see a child with a problem that has become well established. It might be six weeks, it might be six years, or even sixteen years – so there is a routine involved, everyone

knows what's going to happen and everything they see,
touch, hear. Everybody is involved – its like a conspiracy to
make sure it happens again, again and again, so there is a
pattern there and we have to interrupt it, just change the
pattern somewhere, so that sometime in that routine the
usual doesn't happen – something else can happen instead.
So a lot of it is about interrupting patterns that cause an
emotional or behavioural problem.

Labels

Some of our children have been diagnosed and they do
have health problems, and a lot of them have a syndrome –
that's serious. If you look in a dictionary, a syndrome is a
collection of symptoms with no known cause. It's a bit like
lumbago, if you have a bad back and you go to the doctor,
with a bit of luck he will tell you you have lumbago, which
in Latin means your back hurts. It's no help whatsoever in
getting rid of the pain.

So if you have got a syndrome, well all it means is that
you have symptoms, but that doesn't help anybody, so we
don't look at syndromes or symptoms, we think – let's get
this kiddy to take a different view on life, and if you can do
that, magically – say tics disappear. I don't know why the
tics were there in the first place. They are certainly useful
for getting attention when you need it, but when you don't
need that kind of attention, the tics stop.

Sometimes the syndrome ceases. Strange. So no labels,
no symptoms, no syndromes, which is all diagnosis. Really
you are dealing with a person who has a problem that they
can't deal with, which might well be an emotion or a habit,
and in both of these cases you may well find a way to
change things.

The Extra Ingredient

Even though the therapies stand alone in their own right, the fusion of nutrition, massage and imagery together produces effective and efficient results. However, there is an extra ingredient.

Carl Rodgers, the father of counselling, is quoted as saying that his clients were found to improve with his 'unconditional positive regard'. The leading physician of the renaissance, in the fifteenth century, Paracelsus said, 'The most fundamental principle of medicine is love.'

Parents demonstrate their love with the time and attention we ask them to give to their child: massaging gives quality time, actively giving love with their intention and touch. In nutrition, the time and care taken to shop, buy, prepare, cook, present and eat together healthy homemade meals, all that shows love.

Time and attention spent on imagery, practising assignments and perhaps changing negatives to positives, is rewarding and praising the good. One school of thought suggests that there are only two emotions – love or fear. Imagery is actively working on reducing the fear – clearing negative emotions attached to negative events, and actively encouraging positive, helpful habits, emotions and memories.

In some of our literature we show a four leaf clover with the three therapies on three leaves, with love as the fourth leaf. Our strap line has been 'C *love* r House with love inside'.

More of what families liked most:

'Your welcome and positive outlook. The refreshments were always appreciated.'

'Genuine caring aspect. Wonderful calm atmosphere and ambience.'

'The holistic nature and determination of all staff to achieve as much as possible. Its ability to bring about change without numerous sessions.'

'Loved the massage.'

'My daughter gained confidence and had time to herself with people who liked her and didn't frown on either her behaviour or what she said.'

'She enjoyed the attention.'

'The comfortable, friendly, homely atmosphere and the dedication of all those involved.'

'Approachable, very professional.'

'You gave me confidence to deal with my son's problems.'

'The results!'

Chapter 6

Sustained Results

The therapies of nutrition, massage and imagery are taught as self help techniques to use at home. Using them between sessions can bring amazing results in clearing children's symptoms and conditions. They can be continued for lifestyle changes, and therefore produce sustained results.

Two months later – Liam

Liam aged 11: Behaviour, separation, bullying.

Two months later Mum scored 10/10 for service, and in changing the child's condition, and wrote, 'He is like a new child – we have changed the way we eat. Liam is doing well at school; he has won a competition for being a young writer. The family is so much happier and the knowledge I have gained I have passed on to my family and friends.'

Six months later – Eric

Eric aged 10: Behaviour, exclusions and bullying.

Dad popped in to say Eric has had his end of year report. 'All good – not a bad thing in it. He's caught up 2 years in three months since coming to Clover House and he's all set for secondary school now.'

One year later – Jack

Jack aged 10, diagnosed as borderline ADHD scored fidgety from 3 to 7 during sessions. Improved to 8/10 just one year later, concentration from 3 to 6 during sessions and improved to 7/10 one year later, and school improved from 4 to 7 during sessions and to 8/10 one year later

His mother confirmed that her son 'had gained a new life', and she had learnt new skills and knowledge of listening to her son and others.' Others had noticed the change, as well as school, and with no visits to the doctor.

They were still using massages (scored at 10/10). With nutrition, Jack 'was still taking vitamins and aware he feels sick when he eats sweets.' Imagery was also scored at 10/10.

One year later – Rachel

Rachel aged 9: Behaviour, sibling rivalry and school problems. Scored from 1 to 8/10 for temper tantrums after two sessions. One year later Mum reported her child was 100% better, and that it had been 'absolutely wonderful' and 'it had helped all of us.'

Rachel had gone abroad with her aunt on holiday with her sister which they would not have been able to do before. She scored 10/10 achievement on child's condition, and 10/10 satisfaction with the service, and an improved temper tantrum score to 10/10.

Two years later – Casey

Grandmother of Casey aged 13 who had school phobia from bullying, and suffering panic attacks and poor sleep, recorded all three problems at 9/10 on a telephone evaluation, and said that Casey 'was attending college a year early. He still loves his massage and asks for it.'

Nutrition was difficult at first, but got better, and they still try. Casey liked talking to the imagery therapist John, and felt it helped, they have all become more communicative. She said she was very happy with the way things have turned out.

Five years later

Jayne aged 11 had been bullied and had low self esteem, but wrote a thank you card (out of the blue) stating:

'I am enjoying school, and made loads of friends and learnt (with your help) to stand up for myself and stick up for other people. I've been at Brownies for two years, helping kids, which I love. Now I can carry on helping and become a teacher. Haven't been to hospital for two years, through coming to Clover House, I've become much more outgoing, which I think is great. (I'm not sure Mum agrees – sometimes she wishes I was still silent). Thank you so much. You've changed my life and left footprints in my heart.'

Chapter 7

Attention Deficit Hyperactivity Disorder
– Child On Medication –

At Clover House, we found the scores for children attending with ADHD behaviour began with an average score of 1.3/10 and finished at 7.6/10. Other symptoms/problems for children with ADHD on medication, including not sleeping, poor appetite, mood swings, anger, sadness, headaches, being teased, anxiety, sleep walking, bedwetting, weight loss, averaged out at 2/10 and improved to 7.4 /10. With one exception, the average number of sessions was four.

The Problems

Kyle aged 7. His mother wrote that Kyle had violent mood swings, temper tantrums and was verbally abusive. He had always been difficult and got worse at age 4. She had had post-natal depression, and was still suffering this, and wrote that she did not bond with Kyle. He had been diagnosed with ADHD, Dyspraxia (co-ordination disorder) and Dyslexia. He had been taking the drug Ritalin for two years, but his mother thought his problems related to a car accident, and his parents splitting up two years ago.

Kyle called himself stupid. He was not sleeping well and was on the sleeping medication Melatonin. He had been permanently excluded from his primary school due to his physical and verbal aggression.

56

Cameron aged 10. Recommended by their doctor, his mother had written that Cameron was very unhappy and made comments like 'I hate my life', and that he wanted to hurt himself when he became frustrated. He did not cope well with being teased by other children at school. He had been diagnosed as ADHD at age 5 and put on Ritalin since age 6. His mother reported that she had little support, that the school insisted he was 'unteachable' without Ritalin.

Cameron said he got teased about being 'on drugs', and felt sad, got headaches and did not want to feel 'like a zombie'. His mother supported her son in that he was bullied at school and he had been taught to stick up for himself.

Edward (8). Edward's parents moved house when he was 3. He started school at 5, and the teacher was concerned about his behaviour, and after a lot of tests with specialists he was diagnosed ADHD and prescribed Ritalin. Edward was unhappy about taking the drug and being different from the other children, but he was also anxious about not taking it. His parents wanted to do all they could to get him off Ritalin as they were concerned about his progress at school, and wanted him to reach his full potential. He was also sleepwalking.

Nutrition

At Clover House, Kyle's (7) family was advised to stop the sleeping drug and replace it with a natural supplement of magnesium. He needed to eat more magnesium-based foods (such as dark green vegetables, fish, eggs, cereals). Also to stop all citrus foods and drinks. A further supplement of fish oil was given.

He did continue with ADHD medication. He was hardly eating at all, which would cause erratic blood sugar levels, which in turn can cause more aggressive behaviour. Homework was to encourage eating, to eat regularly and to sit together as a family for meals. This should be a relaxed affair, not hurried or challenging. To avoid sugary foods and fizzy drinks, and to have supper at supper time.

At a third session, we gave Kyle's mother a handout about additives, with support on implementing the advice given. We received good feedback that he was eating more, (he had tried fish and chips, lamb, tuna and cabbage) and was sleeping better. Behaviour and concentration had improved. He was taking the magnesium supplement in the mornings, and we asked him to keep a food diary. At the fifth and last session, further motivation was given on implementing changes.

Cameron (10). Cameron's mother was very keen not to give him medication and she herself had started reducing them, as she felt he was an ordinary boy, perhaps a little immature. They agreed to start a gluten- and dairy-free diet, and an intensive vitamin programme. Vitamins and essential fats were given. At the second session two weeks later it was reported that they had done very well with achieving an almost gluten- and dairy-free diet. They reported being off of medication and they both felt happier (although school is not convinced she is right). Support and motivation were given to sustain the changes.

Edward (8). We advised the family that Edward's concentration would improve with a less processed and more varied diet. Our advice was to have porridge for breakfast, and for supper, sausages and pitta bread instead of hotdogs, fresh meat instead of packaged. Plain hand-made crisps are better than other crisps, and to have more fish, rice, two apples and a pear each day. Recipes were given for homemade flapjacks, and a sample menu handout.

Edward and his parents were very keen to try new foods. Two weeks later at a second appointment Edward had enjoyed his new foods, and all homework had been done, with an enormous effort by him and his parents. Congratulations given and further advice included having more magnesium-based foods, try buckwheat pancakes, apricots and kiwi fruit.

We suggested reducing Ritalin to every other day and have essential balance supplements at night. At the third session his parents thought they were 70% there on nutrition. He was not keen on nuts, but loved salmon, haddock, omelettes and blueberries. His mother was advised to speak to the school because one of the children had given out chocolate for her birthday and the teacher had said in front of the whole class, 'I hope you are not going to go mental' which had made Edward cry.

Massage

Kyle (7) was tearful at his first session, and said he was an idiot. We did some massage and he appeared very calm. His mother would try massage at night. At the second session, as he was a bit hesitant, his feet were massaged in a chair, after which he was happy to get on the couch and had a 15 minute massage. At the third session another massage technique was demonstrated to his mother, excluding the feet which he found too tickly.

Lots of reassurance was given to his mother to massage him at bedtime to calm him down. Handouts on massage and sleep were given. At the fourth session he talked about the car crash.

Cameron (10). Cameron's mother already touched and stroked his back to calm him. As there was not much time at the first session, we gave him a hand massage instead.

Cameron said he had had plenty of massages at home, and that he felt OK. He had back, legs and feet massaged. The notes suggested that his mother was good at handling him, and she could always control him at home.

She was going to follow up the school who were offering kick boxing for ADHD children to learn to switch their energy and anger.

Edward (8) came with a plaster cast on his left forearm, and his mother was shown how to massage his upper arm and fingers, then his chest, and tummy, and some reflexology moves were shown. Edward used to be massaged as a baby, and his mother took to it really well, so was confident of adding it to their bedtime routine. A massage handout was given. Massage continued at a further session, which he enjoyed. He said he did not want to go home. Reflexology points were shown to help with rehabilitating his arm.

Imagery

Kyle (7). While in the garden at Clover House, Kyle was able to talk about the car crash and his parents' separation. We had three sessions for each topic. Imagery was based on a cloud taking away his problems and raining them into the ocean. Kyle then played with the spinning disk which got faster and stronger with time, while being given suitable messages about keeping going. At the second session Kyle was introduced to the Babushka dolls, where the second to last doll had an upset face, which led to the story that something went wrong, but she got over it.

When asked about school, he hid his face, grimaced and did not speak. He said his first day was bad, but no details, so a 'rewind' (a technique to clear the emotional element of a memory) on the first day of school, with Kyle first watching himself as young Kyle, and then reliving it backwards. He was happy to attend at the third session, but when school was mentioned – he said 'Not that again', and hid his face.

Although we tried to do some work, he pulled away. At the fourth session Kyle's mother retold a sad tale of physical abuse which started when Kyle was born, which she said she might have blamed on Kyle. Work was completed with his mother, a rewind on first time abuse, and installing a good image on her life since, reducing bad memories and increasing good memories. At this session Kyle was able to start some work, but again resisted.

He was asked if he was scared, which he immediately agreed to, and the therapist and Kyle did simulated screams together. It was noted that he appeared to get agitated when asked about how he felt. He wanted to play with a ball, so we agreed on condition he would listen to a story about a boy who was scared to do something, and how he got round it.

At the fifth session Kyle was happy and deliberately tapped the therapist on the knee. Working with Kyle on his own in the Clover House garden, he was able to put his hand on the back of the therapist's fist and allow the other hand to be held, and he listened, but then withdrew. Kyle played with the ball he liked, and when another child turned up, Kyle was introduced formally and asked to shake hands – which he was happy to do and they went off and played well together.

With Cameron (10) rapport building was sufficient in the first session, although it was noted that his mind had wandered. He did not know why he was attending, but his mother said to make him happy. The introduction to imagery was to imagine a leaf with a droplet of water with an explanation from Cameron. He said he was sitting on the leaf which was prickly and circular, and the water felt wet and slimy. He was able to go 'floppy' and into his special place, which was a five-roomed palace full of dead bodies and skeletons. He was asked to practise this at bedtimes, with his mother encouraging him.

Edward (8) said he did not like numeracy or literacy as they were boring, but he did like science. Some magic tricks were shown to Edward and he demonstrated these to his mother and father. He could not wait to be shown the money machine, which produces a £5 note. On his own, Edward did 'collapsing anchors' on school subjects, and indicated success with numeracy.

Having got interested in the idea of using imagery, he was able to do his 'life story', seeing himself through his mother's eyes – which produced a noticeable effect on him, becoming very quiet and relaxed, which his mother noticed afterwards. With the teachers noticing an improvement, his father was asking about how to get off Ritalin, and he was advised to wait a while.

The Results

Kyle (7). After the first week Kyle was sleeping much better. Gradual improvements were reported throughout the five sessions over two months. By the last session Kyle was off Ritalin, and scored sleep improvement from 2/10 to 9/10 and behaviour from 0/10 to 9/10.

Cameron (10). By the third session, Cameron was off medication, sleeping well and not fidgeting or so aggressive. School reported he had been better. Six months later his mother stated that Cameron started Secondary school drug-free and he had a fresh start. She said she knew the foods to avoid, and it definitely made a difference.

Edward (8). By the second appointment, Edward's school had noticed a difference, and he was no longer sleep walking. One month later he was playing with his brother and no longer hitting him and fighting with him.

Food scores had improved from 4 to 6/10, school improved from 3 to 8/10 and sleep walking 5 to 7/10.

Letter from a referring GP

Dear Clover House,

I have been continually impressed by your team's holistic and patient family approach to addressing children's needs. The imagery massage and nutritional advice brings parents closer to their children and in my own patients' experience, helps them work through the physical or psycho-social problems they have presented to both myself and your service.

Whilst your approach is a novel one and sits outside what traditional NHS services offer, it is filled with common sense. Children need space to explore their own problems and often aren't mature enough to be able to medicalise their issues.

The imagery you use allows the child to express in their own words what is happening inside them and allows you and their parents to understand how their problems affect them and their surrounding families.

The massage of course allows children to relax but more importantly brings parent and child together in touch and, in my own experience, from patients' reports, improve parent child relationships

Of course nutrition is a huge agenda both locally and nationally and your sensible advice on improving the contents of diets not only helps improve stress levels and over-activity but also in my view contributes to keeping children away from the continuous weight-gain poor diet which our society as a whole battles with on a daily basis.

In summary I remain impressed by your team's approach and will continue to refer patients into your service. Your alternative approach to addressing physical and mental health problems in our children is both refreshing and successful.

Dr N. Kerfoot

Chapter 8

Attention Deficit Hyperactivity Disorder
– without medication –

S cores were not recorded for behaviour of children diagnosed with ADHD but not on medication. However the average score for other symptoms or problems, including sleep problems, sadness, constipation, fidgeting, lack of concentration, school problems, anxiety, and lack of confidence, were 2/10 at commencement and improved to 8/10 after an average of 3.6 sessions at Clover House.

The Problems

Troy aged 5. Troy's mother was worried about the possibility of Troy having autism and had been referred to an ADHD specialist, but before starting medication she had been looking for help, and found Clover House.

She wrote that Troy would not sleep in his own room and was afraid of the dark, restless and uncomfortable, and that he often took one to two hours to get to sleep. They had tried sleeping medication, but stopped. He had been diagnosed with speech and ear defects when aged 2.

Leon aged 7. Leon's mother wrote that Leon had been a difficult baby, always crying. He could not sit still. He was diagnosed ADHD at age 3, and at age 5 was put on Ritalin, which made him depressed and constipated. Due to these side effects, his mother was looking for alternative treatments. He also had a diagnosis of Asperger's syndrome, and had some obsessive compulsive rituals before bedtime.

Jack aged 10. Jack was diagnosed as borderline ADHD and came with pages of reports from paediatricians and child psychologists with the suggestion of the drug Ritalin, but his mother was reluctant to accept the diagnosis and refused medication. Jack thought school was boring, and had been bullied. He had had two ear infections by the time he was aged 1.

Nutrition

Troy (5). Troy's mother was very keen to learn about nutrition, additives and colourings. A book 'L is for labels' was given. Advice included having no chocolate or peanut spreads, no citrus fruit or fruit flavourings. They were recommended to eat more fish, try mixing it in baked potato or with a crispy topping, and to introduce nuts and seeds. Handouts and a menu plan were given, and an essential balanced diet prescribed.

A week later Troy reported liking his new eating plan. Relatives had given him white packet rice and chocolate, and when he got home he was very hyper and twitchy. His mother had cleared all her cupboards of 'no-good' foods after reading the labels book, and had taken it all on board. Further suggestions were to try buckwheat pancakes, kiwi fruit and to continue with supplements.

Leon (7). At the first session we suggested a change from cow's to goat's milk, to eat an apple a day and have children's vitamin and mineral supplements. Later it was recommended that he progressed slowly to a gluten-free diet with higher nutrients. Leon himself noticed if the diet changed, and he got 'bad' when having chocolate. This meant that he did not eat foods at parties etc., but he did this willingly, knowing he would have his own food when he got home.

Jack (10) only liked carrots and sweet corn, he was already having essential fatty acids, so a children's multivitamin was prescribed. Lots of handouts were given, together with a star chart for trying new vegetables.

At the second session Jack had earned five stars for five different vegetables. He had tried lasagne, stew, leeks and turnips. His mother reported improvements and that he no longer asked for sweet things. We suggested he has more fish and nuts.

At a third session Jack was eating more and continuing to earn stars for trying new foods. His mother said he had had biscuits twice, and she had noticed a difference within half an hour with him being irritable, lacking concentration and fidgety. Homework was to try nuts again, and that he must have one apple, one banana and one other fruit daily, as well as two or three portions of vegetables a day, and to continue with the star chart.

Massage

Troy (5). It was recorded that Troy's mother was fully involved, keen to help, and to try anything beneficial. Troy's feet were massaged while sitting in a chair and then he moved to the couch, for back, front, arms and head massage and became quite sleepy.

His mother took a turn, and said she thought she would find it helpful, easy and enjoyable. She would incorporate it into his bedtime routine, and use it as a reward for going to bed when asked.

At the second session his mother had only done his feet, but realised as she was not content or relaxed herself, that it transferred to Troy. She decided to have therapy herself.

Homework was to carry on with the feet and incorporate a 'rocking' movement for relaxation. At the third session more reflexology was shown as his mother preferred this to massage. After Mum practising, Troy got sleepy.

Leon (7) started to relax when given a massage while his mother watched. She was shown the colon reflexes on the feet for his constipation.

At the next session his mother reported that Leon had come home from school upset, and she gave him a massage and said she would take away his headache with her hands and throw it in the bin – which she did, and it went away. She also told him that 'it takes away the bumpies' when she did massage with him. After a further session, Leon went into deep relaxation, and she was amazed.

Imagery

Jack (10) dated his problems back to starting school, and a teacher who bullied the class. The bullying included hair pulling. Jack responded immediately to imagery, and a 'rewind' (a technique to reduce the emotional element of a memory) used three times on the hair pulling, but did not fully eliminate it.

EFT (Emotional freedom technique of tapping acupressure points while saying affirmations to clear emotional blocks) was tried. Jack was reluctant at first, but got results by focusing in turn on hair pulling, pain and friends suffering the same. His stress was definitely reduced.

At the second session Jack had noticed the differences and liked them. It was decided to work on fidgeting (even though his mother and therapist agreed it did not seem important). He had used the EFT technique on his own for fidgeting and foot tapping.

His fidgeting was brought into conscious awareness, accompanied by non-stop story telling. More stories were told at the third session and a change of attitude towards English lessons to where he does Maths which he enjoyed. At the fourth session Jack could not think of anything else to improve. Imagery was used structuring good and bad memories. The imagery therapist recorded 'ended session with a very happy client'.

Troy (5) liked the magic coin trick, and the dice trick, then the Babushka doll and story, a set of Russian dolls where the second to last doll has an upset face and a story to show things happen in life, but you can get over them.

Troy got very excited and wanted to do the tricks, and his attention was caught by the idea of installing a 'dream arm' (a suggestion that as soon as his arm feels it is in bed, lovely dreams will happen).

Even that did not seem to relax him. So the therapist used his own body language to relax Troy, who 'spaced out', which delighted and baffled his mother. We suggested to Troy he should enjoy the feeling more often.

Troy could not talk about problems. The dream arm was used again, to allow his teddy bears to act as super-heroes to help in his dreams. While Troy played with crayons, his mother did some 'rewinds' on his birth and several traumatic incidents, and we explained how to use body language to calm him down.

By the third session both Troy and his mother were pleased with progress. His mother was introduced to the idea of future planning and how to introduce new things by finding similarities then mentioning small differences.

Leon (7) said he had three scary nightmares 'too scary to tell', so he was given a dream catcher. He developed his 'special place' imagery to practise every night. He loved being told stories, and he knew all the Pokemon monsters and told stories about them. During the sessions Mum used some imagery to help her deal with how her husband had left the family.

Results

Troy (5). As she was leaving the first session, Troy's mother said she was delighted with their visit and would be telling other parents in his class. She had read parenting books and felt she was making progress.

By the third session she reported that the bedtime routine was no longer being controlled by Troy, and he went happily to sleep by himself.

After three sessions, Troy was getting to bed on own, was calmer and more relaxed, improved from 2/10 to 8/10.

In a telephone evaluation a year later, his mother scored bedtime at 9/10 and quoted that all four family members had benefited. Troy's concentration was better, and he was much calmer. She had gained a lot of information. The family was still eating healthily, and shopped in a much better way.

She said Clover House had helped her to understand

that her son did not have ADHD, and the interviewer commented that Troy's mother had been highly complimentary.

Jack (10). After one week, Jack's teachers told his mother his concentration had improved. By the fourth session Jack said he felt more clever and happy. His mother had changed his previous high sugar and junk food diet beyond recognition, eating healthy food increased by 80%, and she was thrilled, especially by all that she had learned about food and cooking.

The therapist had written, 'I am over the moon at Jack's progress and his calmness and new-found ability to concentrate. Could not wish for a better outcome.'

At this session Jack said he had done some homework the other day, which would have been impossible a few weeks ago, and would have ended in tears, but which he did easily.

Scores improved fidgeting from 3 to 7/10, concentration 3 to 6/10 and school 4 to 7/10.

One year later his mother reported to an independent telephone interviewer that her son 'gained a new life'. She confirmed external validations from school, no visits to doctors, and that many people had noticed the change. They were still using massage (scored at 10/10), he was continuing to take vitamins and was more aware. The results of imagery were better concentration, calmer and being able to cope with school.

Score improved for fidgety 8/10, concentration 7/10 and school 8/10. Overall the comment was, 'Can't praise Clover House enough. The primary school teacher felt Jack was a different boy.'

Leon (7). Within a few sessions Leon's constipation had resolved, and the family scored 5/10 for calm, and 8/10 for sleeping. Teachers started noticing the difference and were impressed. Mum was delighted and proud, and said Leon 'had been transformed.' She said she found the dairy- and gluten-free diet expensive, but would not change it for the world, and that the progress made was phenomenal.

Chapter 9

Anger

Anger was one of the most common conditions with children attending Clover House. The average score for anger at commencement was 2.5/10 and improved to 7.7/10 in an average of four sessions. Other symptoms involved with anger included high expectations, sleep problems, school exclusions, being unhappy, hyperactive and hypersensitive, sibling rivalry, bullying, sugar addiction, mood fluctuations, lack of confidence, frustration, anxiety and stress, boredom, lack of concentration and of thinking ahead. Scores for other symptoms improved from an average 3.2 to 8/10.

The Problems

Neil (12), came for his 'temper and frustration'. His mother wrote he had always had this, it was proving difficult, and Neil himself was concerned. Years ago the child minder had said she thought it was because his mind was ahead of himself. His mother had worked full time until he was aged 10 and she tried staying at home, but then thought she was too focused on him, and changed to working part-time.

Liam (12). His mother wrote the problem was anger and behaviour at school – he had been given six weeks to change or he had to leave school. He had become the class comedian and was generally disruptive, but if accused, felt unfairly blamed and answered back. If he asked for things and was told no, he became very angry, and he was playing his mother and father off against each other. It was said he had obsessive compulsive tendencies involving rituals about doing his hair and getting off to school. He had night terrors and nightmares. His parents were going through relationship difficulties.

Andrew (5) came to Clover House for his behaviour problems. He had gone through three schools and was under threat of possible exclusion now. His mother reported he was always demanding, and 'created when with others'. He said he was angry with school because the teachers were horrible to him.

Nutrition

Neil (12) often missed meals, especially breakfast and lunch at school. When asked why, he said he got up late, and that there was not enough time to eat lunch, especially if going to a school club. If he did eat it was crisps and chocolate. So we gave Neil an explanation about the effect this would have on his blood sugar levels and how that would make him feel in a bad mood and short tempered. It was also explained how he needed to eat properly as he would be growing very quickly.

Talking about the school lunch hour, he was given lots of ideas for a big breakfast, and told he would have to get up earlier. We suggested a healthy snack before his football training. Ways were given to increase his fluid intake to at least 2 litres a day. A blood sugar handout was given.

At the second session he had been getting up earlier and having breakfast, and a sandwich for lunch, good snacks and drinking more. He said he looked forward to eating now. He was doing cooking at school. He was encouraged to continue.

At the third session, within one month Neil had grown, and was still doing well with nutrition. Further suggestions were to have even larger portions and extra snacks before training sessions.

Liam (12) was missing breakfast because he took a lot of time doing his hair. He did not like vegetables. He would make himself scrambled egg as a snack after school. We explained to Liam and his mother about low blood sugar levels which could evoke a stress response, and production of adrenaline which could cause him to be aggressive and angry. We suggested that he would have to get up fifteen minutes earlier to have a cooked breakfast. We also explained he could feel angry because he was not eating enough for his age and growth spurts, and to increase his food with double the amount of sandwich fillings, and to have cheese toasties instead of sweets and biscuits. We asked him to try vegetables fifteen times to adjust taste.

At the second session Liam came with his grandparents. He reported that he had been getting up earlier and having toast or cereal for breakfast, and generally following advice. He was reminded to include protein for breakfast, and in snacks throughout the day. Still to try vegetables. These issues were repeated at the third session.

Andrew (5). After discussion, Andrew was given advice on chocolate, but told he didn't have to stop eating it altogether, 'because the bit that made him naughty he could control.' We also suggested that he think about what was said, and talk with Mummy and Daddy about it, since it would be nice to use his energy in other ways. The family was given a menu sheet to use for a week, and information about additives. We prescribed children's vitamins. At the second session he had decided not to eat chocolate at all. He was drinking more water, and all advice was being followed.

Massage

Neil (12) was amenable to massage as his grandfather already massaged his feet. So his feet were massaged during a session at Clover House, and Neil relaxed while chatting with Mum about his frustrations.
He said his mother and father had high expectations of him. His mother was asked to read our booklet and continue with the foot massages during the week.

At the second session Neil was asked what goes wrong with his relationship with his mother and he said she nags. His mother said he would only do things such as home-work in his time and his schedule. We gave a brief explanation of talking adult to adult (rather than the dynamics of parent to child as in transactional analysis psychology) and suggestions of compromises, more positives than negatives, and only asking once then waiting for a response.

Liam (12). Liam's feet were massaged, but his mother had painful hands and said she could not do massage at home. A flower remedy sheet was given.
His grandparents were shown metamorphic technique

which is quick and easy to explain and do (without any pressure on hands for mother).

At the third session, Liam's mother explained that she was separating from her husband again. However they had great faith in the flower remedy.

Andrew (5) was eager to get on the couch and chose some coloured massage oils. A massage routine was demonstrated to mother and father, and Andrew said he enjoyed it. Homework was to continue at home. At the next session all reported enjoying this and his parents were asked to continue to use massage.

Imagery

Neil (12) came across as self possessed, fluent and confident, but had outbursts of temper. The 'lioness' (imagining having the powers of a lioness for confidence) was tried but Neil was not impressed

So this was followed by imagining the energy from his 'hara' (abdomen), which he liked and agreed to practise and use. He seemed preoccupied by his own thoughts. When he was 'back in the room' the test results showed he found it more difficult to get angry – but there was still something there. When he accessed his anger there was a spinning sensation from the emotion. So this feeling was treated by imagining it physically and holding the ends of the axis, turning it over, and replacing it with a new emotion. He said it was different.

Some improvement was recorded at the next session. His over-competitiveness was still breaking through. We told him stories about rugby and cricket, and walking when the ref or umpire said so, and about how good and bad calls get shared out. He was asked to choose a good role model for his behaviour, made an image and got inside it, noticing how it felt to have control. He then watched an image of himself about to go over the top, and got inside the imagined role model and calmed himself down.

Liam (12). With discussion it was found that Liam's anger started at Year 6 in primary school, and his anger was expressed by screaming, swearing and hitting 'stuff'. We asked him to visualize his 'special place', which was his youth club where he could go outside and play football, him and his friends having a laugh.

Stein's clenched fist technique was explained as a tool to capture anger in the fist and then letting it go. Liam was to practise this and combine it with taking deep breaths in and exhaling slowly. He also imagined himself not speaking out in class, even though he believed the teacher was being unfair, and later, as a means of releasing anger, to scribble over a face that represented the teacher.

He attended the next session on his own and reported he had more control over his anger, and had used the two techniques from the previous week. He talked about what happened when his father said 'No' and he had had a tantrum – he felt the anger in his heart and back. To release it, it came up into his throat and he shouted to let it out. An explanation of EFT (emotional freedom technique of tapping acupressure points while repeating statements) was given, and a handout for practice at home on his own.

At the third and final session he reported using the tapping quietly to himself instead of having a go at the teacher. He developed the face scribbling into sticking a face on his punch bag and giving it a good punch.

Andrew (5). Rapport was gained with lots of fun. Andrew introduced his soft toy dog, and explained that the dog was scared of strangers. His parents were asked to *tell* him to do things, not *ask* him. The magic book impressed him. He was testing boundaries in the session, and his father was keenly observing. Andrew said 'No' when asked to put his shoes on, so his mother and father were asked to go without him, which quickly resulted in him putting them on. A book was given to his parents, 'How to talk so kids will listen'.

Results

Neil (12). Neil's scores improved – anger from 3 to 6/10 and high expectations from 3 to 9/10. In a later evaluation his anger score had improved to 8/10. Mum was 10/10 happy with the service and wrote she most liked that it was friendly, local, tackled issues and it worked. How many people benefited? 'Mum, Dad, Neil himself, grandparents, friends and football team – about 25-ish.'

Liam (12). Liam's mother reported at the third session that he was a completely different boy, which she put down to the flower remedy, which he put it in his water for school, and sipped when needed. He was not fidgeting so much when he took the drops. He was generally calmer and went to bed without an argument and was sleeping OK. Scores improved: Anger from 1 to 7/10, behaviour at school 3 to 5/10; healthier eating 3 to 7/10, and sleep 3 to 10/10.

Andrew (5) himself reported he was fine now. His parents seemed happy and said he was doing well. They scored happy from 2.5 improved to 9/10. A month later they sent an email saying that he had progressed well at his new school, and had just spent the half-term at a holiday club and did not react with violence. He made friends easily, having a good time. They felt he was a 'normal' five-year-old boy, and wrote, 'Continue the good work, you are a real lifeline to parents who feel they just can't take any more. Best wishes, and in the best possible way, we hope we don't need to see you again!'

Parent's Letter after treatment for Anger

Dear Clover House,

Andrew has been progressing well since leaving his old school in July of this year. New school holiday clubs and a new school seem to have brought about the change in circumstances Andrew needed to feel happy and secure.

Andrew has just spent the October half term at another school holiday club, and did not react with violence, made friends easily, and generally had a very good time. We now feel that Andrew's behaviour is that of a 'normal' five year old boy, and that he no longer needs the special care from Clover House, but hope that the 'door is left open' should he have more difficulties in the future.

Both my husband and myself would like to thank you all for the assistance you gave us over this very difficult time, and for helping us remember how to love our son.

Continue the good work, you are a real lifeline to parents who feel they just can't take anymore.

Very best wishes and, in the best possible way, we hope we don't need to see you again!

Chapter 10

Anxiety

Anxiety was one of the five main issues for children coming to Clover House. The average score for anxiety at the beginning of sessions was 1.6/10 and finished 7.6/10 in an average of three sessions. Other symptoms included problems with sleep, concentration, school, being unhappy, lack of confidence, and independence. The average score at commencement was 2.7/10 and improved to an average of 7.6/10.

The Problems

Sarah aged 14, had been having physical, fit-style anxiety attacks for five months, when 'her muscles tense and she shakes, and loses her balance, which makes her tired.' After medical advice from the doctor and hospital this had been diagnosed as anxiety attacks due to emotional difficulties. Sarah had been adopted, and her adopted mother reported she had been severely neglected by her birth parents, and she had experienced the loss of her adopted father. The attacks began after the divorce of her adopted father. They happened many times a day and in her sleep, and she got very upset when asked about them.

John aged 4. John's mother wrote that he suffered from anxiety, negative thoughts, sibling rivalry, nightmares, and was worried about school and cubs. She continued that he had been a demanding child from birth, he always seemed hungry and never satisfied. He cried a lot, it took six months before he slept through the night, and he had always been sensitive to loud noises. She also said he set himself very high standards which led to frustration.

Millie aged 6. Her mother had written that Millie 'was a worrier, she lacks confidence and has low self esteem. When her worrying reaches a peak she worries about extremely trivial things, gets very anxious, starts stammering and is currently bedwetting.'

Further information included getting herself extremely confused, such as indicating not making the walls dirty if you have dirty hands, but if she touched a wall, was apologetic and concerned. If asked a question such as 'What did you have for lunch today?' she would say, 'I'm not sure, I think . . . I can't remember. I don't want to lie,' and go on an on.'

She worries about stepping on things, and has started obsessing about things. She had been hurtful towards her mother and preferred to be with her father. She has a six-month-old brother. In her first session she said she wanted her mother to be somewhere else, that she did not like her mummy because she had a fat bottom. She also said she did not know if she loved her mummy or not. Millie had seen her aunt who had cancer 'wired up in hospital.'

Nutrition

Sarah (14). We suggested to Sarah that she keeps a diary of foods, moods and stressors to help towards seeing a pattern or cause of attacks. Her diet was generally good, although a more substantial breakfast was suggested to level blood sugars, to have fruit at lunch, and more vegetables at teatime. A blood sugar level handout was given and supplements of magnesium, Omega 3 oils and adult multivitamin and minerals.

At the second session she had forgotten to do a diary, as it had been the holidays, but she had eaten more vegetables. Advice from the first session was re-emphasised, including to eat more magnesium-containing foods to reduce stress levels, balance blood sugars and being naturally calming. The third session again emphasised a healthier diet and putting recommendations into practice.

John (4) had a good appetite and enjoyed a wide variety of foods cooked at home. Suggestions were to have larger breakfasts incorporating whole grain carbohydrate (whole meal toast, porridge oats) and protein (eggs, bacon, baked beans, nuts and seeds). He should have a bedtime snack, all juices should be diluted with water, and as weight was not an issue he could have homemade cake and flapjack for snacks. A blood sugar handout was given, with magnesium supplements for relaxation.

At the second session we discussed eating organic food, and giving him foods he liked, but gradually adding more healthy foods (i.e. berries and bio yoghurt) and reducing the amount of honey, sugar, etc.

John's mother had a query on magnesium, which he did not like, so it was suggested to add it into savoury foods. At the third session John had tummy aches at teatime since starting reception school, and he would not eat any tea. His mother was asked to increase breakfast and lunch, relax tea time with perhaps just a ginger biscuit to settle his stomach and give him some energy to get off to sleep. An Epsom salts bath was recommended and a liquid magnesium was given.

Millie (6) gained rapport with the nutritionist and opened up about not liking her mother, so she was asked to go up to mummy and say thank you for bringing her to Clover House to make her better. It was reported she kept crying, and said she was not sure what love was. For homework she was asked to have no jelly babies, no orange squash, to have two bowls of cereal a day, and to ask mummy to give her some supper at bedtime and to spend time with her.

More discussion at the second session, homework was to keep a star chart for eating cereal with milk or apple juice. As she had produced a poem she was asked to write a happy poem for next time. She had earned 10 stars by the next session. Millie said she was worrying about the dinner ladies funny voices, and she did not like worrying about this. She asked if she could do a star chart for worrying and to have a star when she was feeling happier and not worrying.

Massage

Sarah (14). Massage was demonstrated to Sarah's mother to use at home, and she was given massage oils and handouts. (Notes written were not about what had been done, but discussion on the situation.)

John (4). Hands, head, arms and feet were massaged and a handout and some massage oil were given to his mother to continue at home. John said he liked the massage the best last week, and mother had reported having done his feet. More massage was shown while talking next time. A flower remedy was given. At the third and last session, we suggested John should have some exercise after school, and a foot massage before bedtime.

Millie (6) used to enjoy massage as a baby and her mother had had massages which she had enjoyed too. It was explained how massage was helpful for bonding. Her mother was quickly involved in massaging Millie's feet, back and legs. They were given some massage oil, and a handout sheet, and asked to try to include massage as often as possible. They reported having done five massages out of seven nights, and that Millie had really enjoyed them. More massage was shown and mother was encouraged to keep it up.

Imagery

Sarah (14). We explained to Sarah how imagery worked and that personal details were not needed. Sarah said her problems started six months previously, and as a result of questions, she remembered something unpleasant – so a 'rewind' (a technique to clear the emotional element of a memory) was done. A clearing technique was done on the same incident (unknown to therapist) and Sarah thought it had changed things. Her mother suggested next time perhaps it would be best to see her on her own, which was agreed by everyone.

At the second session Sarah was eager to work and appeared more confident and said that the problem had eased over the last week and no longer bothered her. She even had trouble recalling what it was.

She wanted to deal with her 'big' problem, her adoption. She could remember many details of what happened with her birth family and it still upset her. To start with she was shown the Babushka dolls and told a story. (A set of Russian dolls where one doll has a an upset face with an accompanying story about how upsetting things do happen and you can get over them), and got out the crayons.

Sarah was amused and excited by the idea of choosing suitable colours and built up a miniature life story. This was cleared with a 'rewind'. When asked to think about adoption again, she reported it as 'different'.

At the third session Sarah reported that the birth family problems ceased to bother her. Although she could not think of anything else that needed attention, a check was made on structuring good and bad memories. She got to change bad memories to the third person viewpoint, small, grey, dim, unfocused and still in the distance with no sound.

For good memories she changed to the first person, all five senses, bright, colourful movies. Her father who attended this session reported that Sarah still had occasional fits, and so during a walk around the Clover House garden, a sudden 'blow out' – a clearing technique – was done on the fits she was having.

John (4) was helped to discover a way of gaining confidence. As he was a fan of Spiderman, he was asked to imagine being Spiderman and this could be used any time he was feeling anxious, reinforced with the idea that super heroes had amazing powers and could tackle any difficult situation.

Millie (6). With her mother and father present, Millie told all about her baby brother. A dice magic trick was shown and the Babushka dolls were introduced. At the second session Millie had brought a drawing of her family, dominated by a beautiful flower. Her favourite flower was a rose. Discussion included the life history of a flower, bees, butterflies and seeds, and how her aunt was proud of her and she will always remember the wonderful things about her.

Millie had brought a poem, and as it seemed to relate to the 'woman who swallowed a fly' she was entranced with the rendition of the whole song. A help frame was done about seeing her aunt, to which she responded with a big breath and smiled. At the next session, the goal was changed from worrying to sensitivity. We talked about being imperfect and good enough, i.e. specks of dirt, stuffed toys with leaks, her grandfather and psoriasis (which worried her).

Millie closed her eyes and did an imagery based on writing her life story. A fourth session was arranged because Millie was anxious about school. Talk was about the future, and she imagined being there in the first person, so the third person was introduced and seeing herself as older in the future, which she liked. Also the 'lioness' was introduced (imagining a lioness was behind her for confidence), changed to be a bit less 'wild'.

Results

Sarah (14). Sarah's mother telephoned us the morning after their first session, crying, and said she was so amazed as Sarah had woken up a 'different person'. After three sessions, she had more confidence and was going out with her friends. They reported anxiety at 2/10 first session, 4/10 second session and improved to 7/10 at third session.

John (4). By the second session his mother reported things were changing. Previously he would be clingy and upset at going to school. They did not complete any scores, but his mother wrote to say he was more relaxed, and a much happier child and that they had tools to use.

Millie (6). By the second session Millie was reported much happier and said that she loved mummy. Her mother said she was 70% better towards her. At the third session, she said she loved the massage therapist the most.

At the second session they scored relationship with mother from 2 to 9/10 ; fears from 2 to 4/10. At the final session, sensitivity was scored from 1 to 10/10 and Mummy stayed at 9/10.

Parent's Letter after treatment for Anxiety
Dear Clover House

I would like to thank you for helping my 12-year-old son through his stressful problems on starting senior school.

Since January there has been a 90% improvement, he is calm, and can handle problems that arise more confidently now. His school work has improved 100% since attending Clover House and I would like to encourage others to approach you if their child is experiencing behavioural problems or finding senior school difficult.

You are all doing a great job with all the children – you give them love, cuddles, hope and confidence. Also you support the parents as well. Keep up the good work.

Chapter 11

Asthma

All children who attended Clover House with symptoms and diagnosis of asthma for two or more sessions recorded substantial improvement including no further attacks and no further use of inhalers. The average score for those who came specifically for asthma was 2.5/10 and after sessions, recorded improvement to a score of 9/10.

The Problems

Chris aged 10 had been diagnosed asthmatic three years ago, and was regularly using inhalers, every night and nearly every day.

Kirstie aged 5 had been on inhalers since the age of 1. She was using inhalers twice a day and went on steroids when she had a cold.

Ben aged 9. Ben's mother wrote that he needed an inhaler twice a day and steroids at least two to three times a year with each cold. Ben was being bullied at school. During sessions it was found that his asthma started when his Mum and her partner might have split up and he was shipped off to Nan's for a few days.

Nutrition

Chris (10). Although eating a fairly healthy diet, the nutritionist suspected a lowered immune system due to having had a lot of antibiotics and a recent reaction to a flu jab, and he was professionally prescribed children's multivitamins. Mum reported a rash. The doctor had said it was heat rash, but our nutritionist suspected viticaria or hives, an indication of allergic reaction. She advised letting it come out and trust that the body was healing itself by elimination. Chris was asked to cut down on flavoured crisps, reduce wheat and cut down on tea.

At the fourth and final session, Mum said she was so proud of her son because he took to the changes so well, and she hadn't really felt he would do it. She was surprised by how much responsibility he was prepared to take for himself. The nutritionist was very pleased with his progress.

Kirstie (5) was asked to reduce dairy foods, to stop chocolate cereals and to start taking professionally prescribed children's vitamins. It was suggested that she try breathing exercises instead of resorting to inhalers. She came to the next session chewing brightly coloured bubblegum, which led to a discussion about additives. A trip out with Kirstie eating sweets made her 'horrendous', which reinforced the family's commitment with nutrition.

Ben (9). After discussion about Ben's food, it was suggested he reduce dairy intake, avoid peanut butter, reduce fizzy coke, and eat an apple a day. At the second session Ben was given vitamins and a new eating plan. Mum was amazed he bounced back so quickly after the flu.

He felt better having goat's milk, and was gradually improving his diet with more fruit and vegetables.

Massage

Chris (10). Chris and his mother enjoyed discovering how to use this form of healing touch, and they borrowed a massage couch to use at home. Mum was taught a basic reflexology technique using gentle pressure on the part of the feet that corresponds to the lungs and chest.

Kirstie (5). After being shown some massage techniques, Mum and Kirstie did them nearly every day. Because Kirstie mainly came for behaviour problems they were given parenting tip handouts, and Mum made some family rules, such as putting her shoes away or 10p out of her money box! They also decided to copy a school idea of using a happy book and a sad book.

Ben (9). Ben's mother had already learnt massage in her job as a care worker. She was shown a routine and given some oils and handouts to use at home with Ben. Unfortunately she reported not having time for this at home but said he had plenty of hugs and cuddles.

Imagery

At his first session, Chris (10) quickly created a 'special place' during his first session which was a room with a coal fire burning and a soft fluffy armchair. Next time he came he envisaged the asthma as a strong rope around the bottom of his neck, which he imagined his mother cut and burned. The ashes were blown out to sea. A week later he reported he had been using this scenario to control any 'twinges' with great success. At the third session a shark ate the asthma ashes in the sea and became asthmatic, until they passed out of its gills. Drifting into the sea bed, they were transformed 'into nice seaweed'. The therapist wrote in the case notes 'I think that just about does it'. The imagery scenario had completely changed from negative to positive.

Ben (9). Ben's imagery for his asthma was 'like a piece of string pulled real tight' so he got Mum to cut it. It left red marks on his chest, but the string was put in the bin, taken to a garbage dump, and burnt like a charred tube. This broke into pieces, and rats trod on them. More garbage on top ... continuing until the scenario had a positive ending – the bits lived happily until they died and went to Heaven.

Ben still worried that his mother and stepfather might split up again, and described the fear in his chest 'as like a horrible hand with blisters, white spots and cuts on it, squeezing his chest.' He continued with this imagery until it had a positive ending and was asked to practise it at home.

Kirstie (5) came with behaviour and sleep problems as well as asthma. Mum was asked to see what triggered the tantrums, to be more positive than negative, avoiding remarks like 'Don't be silly', and to see her daughter as scared rather than naughty. She was encouraged to make efforts to help her daughter feel secure. Finally we suggested she put some fun into her daughter's life.

Results

Chris (10) cut down on using inhalers by over 50% after the first visit and had no need of them by the third and final session. This was despite Mum, also long-term inhaler dependent, insisting he use his inhaler, and Chris protesting that he didn't need to. He scored his Asthma improved from 2 to 9/10.

For Kirstie (5) sleep improved from 1 to 10/10, aggression from 2 to 6/10 and her asthma from 3 to 9/10. Mum rated nutrition as 8/10. School reported being pleased with Kirstie, and she stopped using inhalers. Mum reported they were going away camping together – something she would not have thought possible. At a review Mum said Kirstie was a different child.

Ben (9) scored his Asthma improved from 0 (he actually said –6) to 9/10. Mum wrote a letter of thanks and stated 'without Clover House I believe our son would still be sad and depressed and not the happy and energetic child he is today. I cannot thank Clover House enough for all the help, love, support and friendship it gave.'

Parent's Letter after treatment for Asthma
Dear Clover House,

When my son first started coming to Clover House he was a different child than he is today. He suffered with asthma – needing an inhaler twice a day and steroids at least two to three times a year with each cold. He was a very stressed child and was bullied at school without mercy. Every small problem became an un-manageable tangle that would send him into floods of tears and distressing rages.

It is hard to tell when the changes occurred. Things started to improve right from the first visit to Clover House sessions. Maybe I started to relax as well. I went to Clover House out of desperation, I knew that some of the blame would rest at my feet, I had to have been doing something wrong, hadn't I? I found that I was wrong, wrong to think that it was all my fault and wrong to think that I would be branded a bad mother.

Prior to Clover House, life was a long and vicious circle, almost every day there would be tears and tantrums caused by bullying and more use of the hated inhaler. My son's school have an anti-bullying policy that enables the teachers to punish the children that are hitting and punching the others. They do not have a policy to help the children who cannot bear to go to school, to more name calling and loneliness.

After the third visit to Clover House my son came home and said, 'I've had a really good day today.' I could have wept with joy. From then on things improved in leaps and bounds.

Life at home is so different now, we do more things as a family. We used to be wrapped up in how next to tackle the headmaster and how to cope with our son's problems, we lost sight of how to enjoy being together and have fun.

Clover House has changed our lives, without it I believe that our son would still be sad and depressed, and not the happy and energetic child he is today. I cannot thank Clover House enough for all the help, love, support and friendship it gave.

Chapter 12

Bedwetting

A good majority of bedwetting symptoms were resolved, almost within three sessions. The average score began at 1.71 out of 10 and improved to 9.8 out of 10. Not all children who had bedwetting problems were treated successfully, especially a few who seemed to have an hereditary condition.

The Problems

Elizabeth aged 8 had been bedwetting three or four times a week for over five years. Mum had tried lifting her out of bed with limited success. Elizabeth had experienced her parents' acrimonious divorce, undergone problems with her father's new partner, and suffered some bullying at school.

Sarah aged 11 had never been consistently dry at night. She had a history of bladder infections, and loss of bladder control night and day. She had had many medical investigations and medication, and numerous courses of antibiotics. An acupuncturist had previously recommended reducing dairy products.

Bailey aged 12 came to help his 'lifelong' bedwetting problem. They had tried all the usual strategies of medication, alarms, relaxation and hypnosis without success. Bailey's parents had separated when he was nearly three, and he had experienced fears and traumas from his mother's ex-boyfriend.

He was also labelled ADHD (attention deficit hyperactivity disorder) and showed separation anxiety with his father. Some bullying was reported.

Nutrition

Elizabeth (8). We suggested that balancing Elizabeth's blood sugar levels throughout the day might help her to control her weight and reduce her stress levels. A change was recommended from cereal to scrambled eggs on wholemeal toast at breakfast time, with an apple mid-day. Lunch changed to a deep-filled ham or chicken sandwich and plain bio-yogurt with added berries. For teatime, we asked her to halve the carbohydrate and have twice as many vegetables. Eating foods rich in potassium might also help (bananas, aubergines, melon, tomatoes, dark leafy greens, spinach, plain yoghurt, salmon, avocados). Epsom salts baths were also suggested to increase magnesium levels to help her relax and sleep more deeply.

Sarah (11). We explained to the family the effect antibiotics have on gut flora and how bacteria is needed for a healthy balance. Advice was to reduce inflammatory foods such as red meat, fried foods, sugar and sugary foods, and to eat pro-biotic foods to encourage the growth of good bacteria (bananas, oats, asparagus, garlic, onions, barley, spinach, chicory). Other advice was to have an oat-based breakfast and a small snack at bedtime to help restful sleep. Supplements of cranberry tablets, bio acidophilus, and a multivitamin were given. It was suggested that all the family aim to try new foods, with a view to increasing the variety of flavours and textures, and to create their own food challenge chart.

Bailey (12) and his mother had explanations of stable blood sugar levels to help regulate moods. This meant having protein-based meals, especially for breakfast, and to have regular balanced snacks throughout the day. Advice included to aim for three to four portions of oily fish a week and drink only water or very dilute fruit juice. High potassium foods were recommended. Fish oil supplements and epsom salt baths were suggested. Also cranberry capsules and B complex supplements were prescribed.

Massage
Elizabeth (8). Mum was shown how to provide a full body massage , and was given a massage handout and oils to use at home. It was reported that two massages had been done at home, and both Elizabeth and her Mum enjoyed it. Elizabeth did a flower remedy for herself.

Sarah (11). Both Mum and Dad practised some massage to help their daughter at the first session and were happy to continue at home to help her sleep. At the next session they were shown foot massage and some reflexology. This showed some emotional upset (apparently some girls were causing problems at school). It was noted the corresponding bladder point on the feet was swollen.

Bailey (12). A range of techniques was shown, and a Bach flower remedy provided. Bailey showed some resentment towards Mum and being older, was not interested in having massage at home from his mother.

Imagery

Elizabeth (8). With some magic tricks we soon established rapport, and Elizabeth imagined her own special place with flowers and a fountain – to visit every night. She brought her toy Tilly to meet our toy and they had photographs taken. We discussed the bullying by another girl and gave Elizabeth the idea that this girl must be unhappy herself, otherwise she would not need to be unpleasant. She might even give up if Elizabeth responded differently. It was suggested Elizabeth could ponder on 'What can I do to help the bully please me more?' At the next session some auto suggestions were given on helping her self esteem and independence.

Although nearly sorted, the bedwetting occurred again following a visit from Dad. Elizabeth was given some ideas of positive re-enforcement about how her mother and father were getting along.

Sarah (11). We showed Sarah some techniques to visualize replacing being wet with being dry. She said she was easily upset by people, so she practised imagining 'custard pie throwing' where she inwardly refused annoying comments.

At the second session we worked on her brother with whom she had problems. A 'carwash' technique (washing him down with rainbow-coloured loving water) was done on him, which she enjoyed. We did a 'blow out' to clear a negative state or habit on her getting upset when blamed for something she did not do.

At the third session Mum and Dad wanted more work on getting on with her brothers. Her way of remembering bad events was changed, making them disassociated, distant, static and uninteresting. Her good memories were changed, to be associated with colourful and bright images. The last technique was 'life is a zip' allowing her to access good memories more easily.

Bailey (12). Some positive affirmations were given to stop Bailey going into anger mode on being teased and called names, accessed with a good positive state of mind when he won a javelin contest. Dad was asked to come to sessions. As Bailey was reluctant, we explained to Mum that sometimes bedwetting could be an unconscious expression of a desire not to grow up while Bailey was listening.

He identified the emotion 'sad' when his Dad (often) broke a promise to see him. 'Sad' was located in his heart, it was grey and the heart fell to the ground and shattered with the 'grey' spilling out. It was easily fixed by Dad keeping his promise, whereupon it changed back to a healthy red.

The Results

Elizabeth (8). By the second session Elizabeth had improved and was having dry nights. She had been bought new bedroom furniture and bedding to celebrate. The bullying stopped and she became friends with the bully. Scores for dealing with bullying improved from 5 to 8/10, and bedwetting from 5 to 10/10.

Sarah (11) became happier throughout the sessions and more willing to talk. She said it was harder to get to sleep when she didn't have massage. By the second session she had been dry for the week. Within three weeks she scored sleep and bedwetting improved from 5/10 and 4/10 both to 8/10. Mum and Dad said that they wished they had come sooner (they had the form for 2 years) as they were so happy with the result.

Bailey (12). After twelve years, within three sessions the bedwetting stopped and both parents pronounced it completely cured after twelve years with the condition. The score given was 2 improved to 10/10.

Parents' Letter after treatment for Bedwetting

Dear Clover House,

When we first came to visit you, we brought along with us a very sad and angry little boy. Casey, a child with learning difficulties and behaviour difficulties, had received no one-to-one support in school since starting in September 2001. As a result of this he was unable to cope in the school environment, was not accessing the learning programme and had become very stressed and anxious.

Casey is a confident and extrovert character and when faced with situations he can't understand or cope with, he doesn't become withdrawn or shy. Quite the opposite, he gets angry and aggressive, shouting and hitting out and refusing to comply. Unfortunately this behaviour gets him into difficulties at school and he has often been restrained by a number of adults. He has also been punished for his behaviour with exclusion from school.

We see very little of this behaviour at home. Probably because Casey feels happy, safe and part of a secure loving family. He understands the home environment, respects the boundaries and has support from four family members.

We just couldn't relate to the Casey we were hearing about at school.

By the time we came to see you, Casey was extremely distressed. He had lost his confidence and was very run down. Casey was at this time only able to attend school for afternoons and just wanted to spend the morning watching videos and eating. He no longer wanted to go for his swimming lessons or his weekly horse riding lesson, activities he used to enjoy. He had started wetting himself and was not sleeping well. It was heartbreaking to watch this little boy 'shrinking' in front of us. We felt unable to help him and felt every time we took him to school we were almost betraying him.

Although Casey wasn't the easiest child for you to work with, we followed the advice you have given us. Casey now drinks goat's milk, has no flavoured crisps and we look carefully at the labels when buying food. Casey is on a course of multivitamins and oil supplements. He receives regular aromatherapy body massages when he seems a little stressed or over tired.

Casey started back at school in January with full support and started visiting Clover House weekly. The difference in Casey has been truly amazing. He is happy, confident and thoroughly enjoying school again. His behaviour, though still challenging, has vastly improved and he has not been restrained or excluded in the seven weeks he has been back at school.

He has stopped wetting himself, is sleeping well and is generally full of beans. He can't wait to get dressed and get into school. He is showing an interest in books, computer games and asking about letters and numbers. Such a change, because he had closed his mind to any learning and talking about reading, writing or numeracy made him react very angrily.

Casey has been invited to tea with three different school friends, has been to two birthday parties and is socialising well with children in his class.

He has received two swimming certificates, has changed to a higher ability riding class and has received a school certificate for 100% good behaviour. He received a glowing report at parents' evening. Students visiting the school again this year can't believe he is the same child. We have our son back. I could go on and on . . . !

Thank you so much for the time you gave us. It was a very healing experience for us all.

With love and thanks.

Casey's Mum and Dad

Chapter 13

Bereavement

Children who came to Clover House having suffered a bereavement in the family came because of its effects, such as anger and sadness.

The average score for anger and lashing out at family members was 1.75/10 and improved to 9/10 after an average of 3.5 sessions. The average score for being happy was 1.3/10 and improved to an average of 10/10.

The Problems

Jacob aged 7. Jacob's mother reported that eighteen months after the death of his grandmother he was still tearful and short tempered. He could not stop thinking about her.

Jessica aged 9 came with her grandfather to 'help her come to terms with accepting the death of her mother two years previously.' She was sleeping with her grandfather, was stressed and 'winding up' her younger sister. Grandfather was stressed after two more family deaths, and battles over custody, access and money issues.

Colin age 6 came for his anger. His mother reported that a month previously his favourite uncle had died by committing suicide. She wrote that 'Colin was very fond of

him and was upset that he could not see him again.' He was
withdrawn and unhappy, lashing out at his parents and
siblings. He did not want to go to bed at night or get up in the
morning. He was not sleeping well and was wetting the bed.

Nutrition

With Jacob (7), we had a discussion about how stress can
affect our feelings, and we explained to him that we would
be working on eating different foods to improve his health
and wellbeing. Advice included not to drink squash but to
have water. A completed menu sheet showed he was eating
a fairly balanced diet. His parents said he ate fast and was
always hungry. He was asked to eat more slowly which
would make him feel fuller. He was prescribed children's
vitamin and acidophilus to rebuild his immune system and
gut flora. It was noted he had dark shadows under his eyes.

Jessica (9). Jessica's grandfather was stressed and not
coping, but was able to talk out his problems. He was given
B complex vitamins and magnesium. In order not to put
more pressure on him, not too many changes were
suggested, just for Jessica to eat more vegetables with a star
chart and to achieve 20 stars.

Jessica talked about her mother at her second session.
She was 'winding up her sister' so it was suggested she see
her little sister like a puppy and help her with kindness and
to include her. They had slipped back a bit at the fourth
session, and were motivated to continue with further
suggestions and vitamins.

Colin (6). Advice included having bacon for his
breakfast, to water down drinks, and to have a banana or

apple midmorning. Suggestions were given for sandwiches (fish and protein) and to have fruit. He was also asked to have fish three times a week, and red meat once a week. No citrus fruits or orange juice. To have porridge before bedtime. Magnesium and B complex vitamins were prescribed. At the next session, motivation and support were given to continue these changes. A positive spin was put on changing school. Colin reported that he did not like taking the magnesium, so it was suggested he dissolve it on his cereal.

Massage

Jacob (7). Mum had done a two-day massage course and was very happy to continue at home. It was suggested they might all share some massage. Jacob relaxed well during massage. Both Mum and Dad massaged him at home.

Jessica (9). It was noted that granddad and Jessica relaxed and bonded well during some massage demonstrations. We asked if he could do foot massages for Jessica and her sister at home. Jessica asked for massages to go on longer. A flower remedy was given to both Jessica and granddad.

Problems were identified with the girls not having any female influence in their lives, and grandfather not having a social life or any enjoyable things for himself, which were talked through. He was reminded to do massages, especially when the girls had been away to visit their fathers, and became harder to manage. The girls enjoyed playing with dogs in the garden.

Colin (6) was unsure at first about having any massage, but with gentle persistence he allowed his feet to be

massaged, which progressed to a full massage demonstration and Mum was keen to have a go. Homework was
to give him massages at home. At the next session it was
reported he had had massages every night. Reflexology was
also demonstrated and Mum expressed a wish to do a
course. Despite a house move they continued doing the
massage. Because of changing schools and being anxious,
Colin came for three more sessions. He enjoyed being
involved in the process of making a flower remedy to take
home and use.

Imagery

Jacob (7). Without hesitation Jacob created his own
'special place' which was Manchester United football
ground where he joined in squad training. He visualized
going there each night at bedtime.

In the second session he imagined himself going through
a door at the stadium where he was confronted by a large
brown bear that wanted to eat him. He killed it with a
sword and fed it to a monster lurking in a bin. A passing
crocodile chained the monster in a cage where it died. It
went to heaven and was happy and still.

Granny came past, unperturbed and went happily to
Australia. The crocodile took Jacob home to meet his family.
Finally, food left by the monster was recycled into plain
paper and sent to school for children to draw a monster on.
(A complete scenario where negative turns to positive.)

Jessica (9). A 'rewind' (to clear the emotional element of a
memory) was done on Mum's death and an autobiography
or life story. At the next session Jessica chose to clear an
upsetting incident with an animal which was 'rewound'.

Further help was done with Jessica on the third session. At the fourth session, help was given to grandfather with 'rewinds' on his own upsetting issues.

Colin (6). With a good response to a couple of magic tricks, Colin was helped to 'rewind' the story about his uncle, which was done twice. He was introduced to the Babushka dolls, and the message that upsetting incidents can be overcome. His father was very surprised when Colin was asked to score 'missing uncle' which he said was 5/10.

Colin was then asked how surprised he would be if he found himself sleeping really well. After consideration he replied 'Very', and was told that was a good answer. A spinning toy was used to show Colin how it recovered from its difficulties and could spin even faster. The Babushka dolls were used again, much to Colin's delight.

Mum reported panicky feelings which she thought Colin picked up on. So she was helped to see her panic and a 'compulsion blow out' (to clear a habit) was completed.

Colin was asked to see himself as being carefree in about a month's time, and to envisage this other self in the future, getting inside him and returning to the present, which he seemed to enjoy.

At the next session Colin wet himself which upset him and stories were told about trouser wetting that ended up as positive experiences. Colin did not want to go to his new school, after bullying incidents at his old school had not been addressed. A 'rewind' was done on this. At the next session it was reported that Colin was now just upset on Monday mornings and help was given with 'writing his life story' to increase his confidence.

The Results

Jacob (7). Within four sessions Jacob scored himself 10/10 with being happy with school and Mum and Dad.

Jessica (9). At the third session within three weeks therapists recorded, 'In came a happy smiling child and a calmer brighter granddad.' Jessica amazed everyone by trying lots of different foods – including a whole jar of cockles. She was getting on with her sister, loved foot and hand massages. Both sisters showed real affection and were more positive. They had six sessions to support them and scored confident and calmer from 3 to 8/10, stop sleeping with granddad 1 to 10/10, behaviour to sister 1 to 9/10 and calmer granddad 2 to 7/10.

Colin (6) enjoyed massage and found the flower remedy helpful. He had painted a picture for the imagery therapist. Scores improved in both lashing out at parents and siblings from 1 to 10/10 and happy also 1 to 10/10.

Parent's Letter after treatment for Bereavement

Dear Clover House,

Though living only a mile or two away, I had never heard of Clover House's existence.

I was at a loss where to find help for my son, who was suffering from severe anxiety following an extremely stressful year. (Joshua's father committed suicide.)

Call it what you will, divine guidance or just plain good luck, I was pointed in the right direction to Clover House by an acquaintance who knew of its existence. The moment we crossed the threshold, I felt the warmth, love and support that exude there. I knew we had found what we needed to help my son get well, and, what's more the support I needed to help him do so.

With nutritional advice Joshua has learnt valuable information that will help him make informed choices about healthy living for the rest of his life, as well as how to tailor his diet in times of stress, to lesson symptoms of stress, anxiety, etc.

My pre-adolescent son didn't always readily accept massage, but once we adopted a brief physiotherapy-type approach it became 'cool'.

The imagery man identifies with children's feelings in a way that seems quite miraculous to me. He seems to have an affinity with their feelings that is awesome. Through fun and magic and lots of well disguised therapy, my child seemed to find within himself that part that had gone astray.

It was hard going at times, but he is now almost restored to the surly burly lazy sort of individual that we know as normal! I never thought I would be thrilled about that!

Both Joshua and I would recommend the therapies at Clover House unreservedly. They are the missing link of unconditional love and care, which is missing in so many facets of modern society.

Chapter 14

Bullying

Clients turning to Clover House suffered a variety of symptoms as a result of bullying. These included lack of confidence, aggression and behaviour problems, as well as poor sleep, and not wanting to attend school. On assessment, average scores for behaviour as a consequence of bullying commenced at 4/10 and improved to 8.5/10 in an average of 3.75 sessions.

The Problems

Carrie aged 14. When asked at her first session what triggered her problems, Carrie said it was from primary school when she was bullied. Her mother had written that her daughter's anxiety and fear 'affected every part of her life, as she worried about everything, and no amount of reassurance helps.' Carrie had a deep fear that her parents would die and therefore slept on the floor in their bedroom, and often woke them during the night. They had tried the NHS and cognitive therapy, 'none of which was really very helpful'. She had been suffering for years, and had developed obsessive compulsive tendencies.

Hilary aged 9. At her first session, Hilary explained she had been bullied by one pupil since the age of four, which had only recently been disclosed. Hilary was afraid to stand up for herself because when she once did so, she was pushed, went dizzy, fell and knocked her head, and had a fit. Hilary was angry, and her grandmother brought her explaining that her mother had been in hospital, and her great granddad had died. She had witnessed her mother having panic attacks, and there were problems getting Hilary to school, complaining that she felt ill. She also suffered from hayfever and eczema.

Andrew aged 15. His mother wrote that 'Andrew is the victim of repeated bullying, and fear is affecting his daily life. Andrew thinks he is a human punch bag. Most times he will not show his anger or emotions until he gets home. He shows it by shouting, throwing things, making strange noises and talking to himself; he is too frightened to go upstairs or sleep alone. He shouts in his sleep, and wets the bed.' He had suffered a severe assault by two boys, which cracked his ribs with internal bruising. Andrew was too scared to attend school. His mother was on her own and in ill health.

Nutrition

Carrie (14) said she did not like eating foods that resembled animals, and she wanted to be vegetarian. She would not eat red meat. There was a need to get more protein into her diet, and to reduce foods containing additives. Carrie seemed interested in eating healthily. She complained of headaches, so was prescribed magnesium and B complex, and Omega fish oil supplements. She was asked to do a star chart and earn 30 stars for trying different vegetables. By the second session she seemed to have a different attitude, and had tried numerous vegetables.

We discussed proteins and recipes, and doing a star chart for fish. At her third session she had attained 22 stars and had tried fish four times in the past two weeks. At the fourth session she came with blocked ears and a sore throat so some ear candles were applied, with some aloe vera drops. We suggested she tried homeopathic tincture of euphrasis. We also recapped on her nutritional requirements.

Hilary (9) liked most foods, and although her diet was generally good, she had quite a lot of sugary foods throughout the day. Advice included changing breakfast from crumpets and porridge to scrambled eggs, ham or smoked salmon and wholemeal toast. She was asked to change to apples for snacks at school, swap puddings for fruit, and increase oily fish to three or four portions a week – as the Omega fats are anti-inflammatory and could help her hayfever and eczema. A vitamin E capsule, broken and applied directly to the skin could help her eczema.

As Hilary did activities most evenings including competitive swimming, nutritious snacks were suggested before and after swimming. It was also suggested that one night a week not doing activities should be a 'recovery' night to have an Epsom salts bath and an early night.

Nutritional advice was given again to her mother (her grandmother had attended the first session) and further recommendations included watering down fruit juices, and completing a new food challenge chart for more vegetables, as she was unreceptive to trying new foods. It was further suggested she could taste test five different apples to see which she liked best.

At the third session Hilary had tried raw carrots with cream cheese, and parsnips, french beans, peppers, cauliflower, and courgettes. She was having bacon and eggs for breakfast, and had tried the apple test. A blood sugar handout was given.

Andrew (15). Andrew's diet was generally good but he was asked to have a more satisfying breakfast such as a bacon roll, porridge or beans on toast for more energy. Recommendations included eating foods rich in B vitamins for energy and stress (wholemeal bread, brown rice, fish, meat, pulses, eggs, etc.) and more foods containing magnesium, helpful in managing stress, i.e. nuts and seeds, brown rice, pulses, eggs, fish, lean meat and leafy green vegetables. Supplements of B vitamins were also prescribed.

At the second session it was reported that mother had not been shopping and they had not followed our recommendations. We encouraged him to try milk other than cow's, and to repeat the foods mentioned at the first session. They had been able to improve the diet by the third session.

Massage

Carrie (14). Carrie's mother had already done a massage course and had sometimes massaged Carrie. They were keen to learn more, so started with a foot massage, and then her mother carried on. More massage techniques were demonstrated and, as Carrie has difficulty in getting to sleep, we suggested doing them at bedtime. Reflexology points for headaches and backaches were shown on the feet. Massage oils, handouts and a flower remedy sheet were given.

At the next session a flower remedy was completed. They had been too busy to do massages at home, so we reinforced recommendations to try during the coming week. As there seemed a little tension between Carrie and her parents, we talked generally about how difficult it is for parents and teenagers as they learn to relate as adults. Some massage had been done at home. Another flower remedy was completed. Her mother was too busy to do much massage at home.

Hilary (10) stayed outside crying while her grandmother tried to get her inside. They were given a flower remedy sheet to complete to keep them distracted. Her grandmother said Hilary liked head massage, so a metamorphic technique (a light stroking and flicking motion around the head) was done. Grandmother said she thought Hilary's parents, being teachers, treated her like a pupil, and scores were done on how she got on with her mother and father. In later sessions with her mother and father, massage techniques to be done at home were shown again.

Andrew (15) had a headache and was pleased to have a face and scalp massage, which enabled him to relax more. He was polite and said thank you.

His mother could not do much body work as her own medical condition affected her hands, but was asked to try. Andrew was rehearsing for a pantomime and they had not had time by the second session to do any homework. They chatted about the school situation and by the third session his previous school had offered to have him back, about which they were happy.

Imagery

Carrie (14) disclosed that when she was aged 4 she broke her elbow badly in a playground accident, and the subsequent medical treatment had been unsuccessful. A 'rewind' – a technique to clear the emotional element of a memory – was done on the broken elbow incident and the bullying.

She was asked about her anxious feelings towards her parents and unconsciously demonstrated how worrying it was. She was shown how to focus attention on this worrying thought, and got it to go bigger, and a 'blow out' technique to clear habits was used to get rid of it.

At the second session she said she felt better, but answered 'Don't know' when asked about anything, so we did 'autobiography' imagery techniques to help confidence and self esteem.

At the third session a rewind was done on something that was bothering her. The 'lioness' was installed (imagining you have the powers of a lioness protecting her cubs) for confidence.

Next the 'dream arm' technique (suggesting that a chosen arm will provide lovely dreams) was used to deal with sleep problems. She used her mother for her super-hero to help her in her dreams.

Hilary (10). Rapport was established, especially while taking photos of everyone. When asked what she was coming for, she thought it was about being argumentative with her mother and father, and explained about a girl who had bullied her at school for years. She was asked to put her left hand on the therapist's right hand to allow the feelings to flow down her arm and into his hand, so that she wouldn't be upset when she talked. She chatted freely.

We told her a couple of stories about being bullied at school and learning how to deal with it, and a fictitious story about living with Uncle Jack who was a school teacher. Homework was for her mother to write up what happened at the session and Hilary to mark it out of 10. (Hopefully this would enable them to share thoughts and some role reversal.)

We discussed the bullying and the possible reasons somebody becomes a bully, and the importance of the response. Hilary was asked to consider 'What can I do to help the bully please me more?' It was found that Hilary thought herself 'not bright' so she was given a confusion technique monologue which gave the message that she had thought herself into a reality where she was not bright. In order to change that reality, all she had to do was change her thoughts. When she was then asked to do an imagery, she said she had chosen to go on an imaginary gallop on her pony instead.

Andrew (15). After describing 'play theatre', Andrew was set up with crayons to play out the day he was badly beaten up, and a 'rewind' was repeated. Talk was then about sleep and a 'dream arm' was set up with a super-hero figure to help. As his brother and his mother attended they all took part in the interventions, and they all did a help technique which seemed to go down well.

At the second session no homework had been done and scores had not improved. More work was done on the bullying, and the 'bad memory' structure, which was changed. At the third session Andrew's mother realised that he had been going out with his friends again. Work was done with his mother to 'move' the way she remembered her past to a better place, and change the way she remembered them, making them disassociated, colourful and bright. After that they both did 'life is a zip' to help access good memories more easily.

The Results

Carrie (14). Carrie's father reported that after the first session she started singing in the car home – 'hadn't heard that for ages'. Her scores for sleep were 2 improved to 5/10, school 4 improved to 6/10 and enjoyment 2 to 7/10. In an evaluation her father wrote that they achieved a happier daughter which made the whole family happier. Carrie wrote that she had a better life, and liked the friendly, helpful, relaxed and informal if not chaotic service – which made it fun.

Hilary (10). After crying and not wanting to come in at the first session, Hilary said she couldn't wait to come back. Within 3 sessions and one month scores improved: Mum 5 to 10/10, Dad 4 to 9/10, unwell 3 to 10/10, and angry 6 to 9/10.

Andrew (15). At the third session Andrew's scores improved: confidence improved from 2 to 6/10, bedwetting 2 to 7/10 and fear 1 to 7/10. His mother said the imagery had been 'amazing'.

Parent's Letter after treatment for Bullying

Dear Clover House,

Words alone could never express the gratitude I feel for all the kindness given to us on our visits to you. Sophie was at an all time low in her life and it broke our hearts to see her like that, so really all your care and love not only helped Sophie but it was a great source of strength for me too, and I too looked forward to our visits to Clover House.

It warmed my heart to see Sophie relax and smile, she hadn't been doing much of that. There really must have been a special magic in the magic room. It didn't take long and Sophie began to regain some confidence and stood up to the bullies in school, in fact one became friends and even went to church with Sophie a few times. Sophie is cured of being bullied, but as you know she still has many complex emotional needs due to the head injuries, and I am sure that had I been able to get her to you sooner this would have improved too beyond all shadow of a doubt. But as you know our life is a soap opera and continues to be so.

Sophie and I love you all and will never forget you. I try to spread the word about Clover House to all I meet, especially to families with youngsters in need. I tell them about your tranquil haven of healing.

God bless you all

All our love, from Mum & Sophie.

Chapter 15

Concentration

We were able to help all the children who came to Clover House with reported concentration problems. The average score commenced at 3.6/10 and improved to 7.3/10 in an average of 3.3 sessions. Concentration issues came with other symptoms including sleep, anxiety, anger, ADHD, parents' separation, school and boredom.

The Problems

Martin aged 9 came with a two-page list of symptoms including a possible diagnosis of ADHD (confirmed during sessions), falling behind at school, not retaining instructions, easily distracted, unable to keep still, and poor concentration. Mum had divorced Dad when Martin was aged five and starting school.

Carl aged 12. Mum wrote on our questionnaire that she was 'desperate for help and understanding.' Carl had always suffered from a low attention span, and could also be disruptive and too rough. This had happened at playgroup and Mum was told he would grow out of it – but this had not been the case. Mum had tried social services and Carl's school for help, but he continued to have problems for which she felt she needed help.

James (7) had experienced a family breakdown with his elder brother and father moving to another country. Mum reported his moods had worsened over the past year – he got angry and was hard to control, had restless sleep and was struggling with school work. The school nurse had assessed him as OK, but Mum said she was constantly concerned about him.

Nutrition

Martin (9). Mum and Martin listened to an explanation of how sugar and sugary foods such as biscuits and white cereals affected mood and concentration.

At first it was suggested they adapt his cereal breakfast by adding nuts and seeds and yogurt to make it more sustaining. Also to have a protein and carbohydrate-based snack at bedtime to prevent blood sugar levels falling too low during the night. We explained that new foods need to be tried at least fifteen times. Mum was given a recipe for a five-vegetable tomato sauce. They were given a blood sugar balance handout, together with supplements of magnesium, Omega oils, and junior multivitamins. Further sessions included encouraging Martin to wean himself off sugar.

Other discussions included trying different snacks such as pilchards on toast, and as he did not like the taste of the magnesium tablets, to crush it in yogurt or tomato puree. Handouts of healthy snacks and lunches were given.

At the third session we suggested Martin use a brain gym cross crawl exercise to help improve balance and focus, and gave him handouts on fruit and vegetables and ADHD.

Carl (12) was asked to have two different kinds of cereal, one for breakfast and one 30 minutes before bedtime. Also to change from white to brown bread, eat oily fish twice a week, and to eat lots of nuts and seeds (but not peanuts or pine nuts). We suggested sometimes having grilled bacon and poached egg for breakfast and an apple mid-morning at school. No Chinese foods, sauces, coffee, or fizzy drinks.

At the second session, advice included having some porridge, manuka honey, and different fruits. Try milk shakes, using full fat milk and real fruit, and to try coloured rice.

At the third session Carl still did not like brown bread, so we suggested trying rye bread, fresh sardines, grilled or poached kippers. Further suggestions were to try different sorts of milk, oats, soya or rice and to keep up the brown foods, i.e. rice, pasta.

James (7). Mum admitted going to extremes with food, junk food one week, and extra healthy the next. James was found to be rather hyper, due to lots of additives in his diet, so suggestions included leaving out fizzy drinks, sweets and chicken nuggets from his diet, and eating more chicken, vegetables and fish. Homework was to use the star chart and get 10 stars for fish and vegetables and to reduce computer game time. A magic book was used, and James was told the magic would not work if he ate magic draining foods (junk). At the third session James recalled all the new foods he had tried.

Massage

Martin (9) was eager for massage and it was found he had tension in his right shoulder blade. Mum mentioned her own tension, so breathing deep into the abdomen was explained. They were given some oils, a massage handout and our Clover House booklet to continue massage at home. They reported doing massage every other night and that it helped Mum relax too. As there had been some disruption with Martin after staying with Dad, Mum photocopied some pages from our booklet about reducing time spent on TV and computer games so that Dad was aware too.

Carl (12) loved being massaged. Mum did it some 2–3 times a week.

James (7) jumped onto the couch at his first session, and although he was fidgety, Mum was shown how to do some massage – with James wanting Mum to do some 'chopping' on his back. They had instructions to do some massage at home and take a look at some flower remedies. We had a chat about strategies for bedtime, including using lavender oil in the bath. As James was angry after a visit from his Dad, Mum suggested buying some sort of punch bag for James to take out his frustrations – instead of hurting his brother or sister.

Imagery

Martin (9). Rapport was easily gained and sleep was the first problem tackled. A 'dream arm' was installed (with the suggestion that when the arm knew it was bedtime it would help with lovely dreams), with Martin giggling furiously as he learned to use his imagination more effectively. He chose 'my family' for his super-hero helper in his dreams.

As he was then quiet, Mum did several 'rewinds' (to clear the emotional element of memory) on incidents that were bothering her as she had been near to tears several times.

Martin was seen on his own at the second session, and he agreed he had trouble accepting his parents had split up. Imagery was used of someone he knows who seems to be able to deal with life's blows. He chose a friend, so an anchor was set and then Martin was asked to step inside his friend to deal with his problems. His face lit up and responded by saying it felt great.

Martin then learnt a new way of recalling unpleasant things and that he could use this on his own. As he was still worried about coping with his feelings, we set up a way to help him deal with coping well over being unable to cope.

At the third session, because Martin did not want to move house, imagery work was done on the future, and he learned to see himself dealing with things in the future and how to access an appropriate positive emotion. Mum was also helped by decreasing her bad memories and increasing her good memories.

Carl (12). Carl admitted he did not like Maths or English lessons, especially the teachers. So he was helped to imagine History lessons (which he likes) and moved his idea of Maths and English over to where he did History. He laughed and said he would like to keep this way of thinking, and was helped to do a permanent change.

During discussion Carl said life was boring, especially as he lives miles away from any friends. He was asked to build up the idea of being bored at home and did a 'compulsion blow out' sending the idea through him and behind him forever at the speed of light (to clear a habit).

At the second session he did general work on school, moving images around to where they worked better. He imagined himself in the next month or so enjoying life. He was shown the Babushka dolls (one of the dolls has an upset face and a story that sometimes upsetting things happen and we can get over it) which he pronounced 'cool'. At the third session advice was given about setting up a specific location in the house for negotiation and discussion, and rules for time-outs if the discussion got heated. Help was given with being 'laid back'. He imagined having 'good days' and moved 'laid back' to where he kept 'good days'.

James (7). After showing James a dice magic trick – with promises to show him how it worked after the session, James did not want to listen much. He agreed he did not sleep well, and got down to some work bringing his teddy as a super-hero to help him in any bad dreams.

At the next session James was playing with a squeezy ball, so we told him a story about it being a sea anemone which taught people to relax and feel confident. At the third session crayons were used to set up the family experience and understanding of other people's point of view.

The Results

Martin (9). By the second session Mum reported Martin as generally calmer, and that changes in the diet were having an impact. Martin reported things were better, and at the third session he said things were a lot better. When asked about school he said it was easier. Scores improved on both anxiety and worry from 0 to 10/10 , sleep 4 to 8/10 and concentration from 4 to 7/10.

Carl (12). At the second session after doing work about school, Carl said he was much better and that school was 'fabulous', and that he had forgotten to be bored. He scored anger from 1/10 improved to 7/10 and concentration from 2/10 to 7/10. On an evaluation Mum wrote 'In a short space of time my son made a dramatic improvement in his overall behaviour and became a much happier person.' She scored 10/10 satisfied with our service and most liked 'finding someone who for once understood our problems, and such quick results.'

James (7). Showing James the magic book worked and he was eager to report that he had gained 14 stars the first week. Mum reported he was more observant and talking sensibly most the time. Scores were aggression which improved from 2/10 to 6/10, sleep 4 to 8/10 and concentration 4 to 6/10.

Chapter 16

Confidence

The average score of children suffering a lack of confidence started at 1.8/10 and finished at 7.5/10 over an average of three sessions. Other symptoms included anger, worry, poor sleep, fear of being in crowds and not being friendly, and unable to be with friends, bedwetting, bullying and anxiety. Symptoms improved from an average of 2.7/10 to 7.7/10.

The Problems

Peter aged 11. Peter's mother wrote that he had emotional difficulties at secondary school, and that he had dyspraxia, ADHD (Attention Deficit and Hyperactivity Disorder), and autistic tendencies. He found noisy environments difficult and did not like teachers shouting.

Confidence was scored at 0/10. He could not talk to the therapists and hid behind a large teddy bear.

Angela aged 6. Andgela's mother had driven past Clover House, but then came in, completing a form stating that her daughter lacked confidence and was angry. She did not make friends easily, perhaps because she had been bullied at a previous primary school, and was moved when teachers did not do anything about it. She was also scared of dogs, dating from when one got loose in the playground when she was younger. At the first session her mother described bereavements in the family, divorce and arguments with her mother-in-law, resulting in Angela not seeing her grandmother.

William aged 12. William's mother recorded that he had very low self esteem, aggressive behaviour, and needed lots of attention. The head of Year Seven thought something was amiss, and tests were being arranged. Mother wrote a letter informing us that he liked to rule the family, he often caused a fuss about clothes, and that by the age of three he was very unsociable. He would not join any clubs even if it interested him, such as swimming. He did not want to be told what to do. He did not like socialising, and did not care what adults thought about him, but he did worry what people his own age thought of him.

Nutrition

Peter (11) said he felt sick after every meal. This was thought to be due to catarrh caused by his obsession with cheese, so he was asked to cut down on cheese. Although he ate plenty of fruit and vegetables, it was thought he was lacking in minerals, so he was asked to take a liquid multivitamin and mineral drops, and keep taking his Omega fish oil, and some elderberry tonic. He only talked behind the large teddy bear, and apparently his world evolved around his teddy bears at home. Homework included cutting out all cola fizzy drinks, to eat fish and chicken, and have porridge for breakfast and half an hour before bed. He was asked to eat nuts and seeds, and brown rice.

He was given 10/10 for effort at the next session. He had tried all the foods suggested and cut down on unhealthy foods. Homework was to continue with the same foods and to keep painting as he seemed to relax with this activity.

Angela (6) would not eat any vegetables and the only fruit she liked were apples and bananas. This had happened since her sister was born. The blood sugar balance diet was explained, and it was suggested she have an egg for breakfast, and protein at lunch and tea, which would help her feel calmer. Angela was given an explanation as to why she needed to eat fruit and vegetables, and a five-vegetable tomato sauce recipe was given to mother.

Homework included eating wholemeal bread, brown rice and pasta, and to drink plenty of water. The blood sugar handout was given together with children's multi-vitamin and mineral supplements.

At the second session Angela had been trying lots of new foods, though she was still having sugar-coated cereal for breakfast, and did not like brown bread. She was asked again to have a boiled egg as well as cereal for breakfast, and try to have wholemeal toast soldiers. Mother was encouraged to take her daughter food shopping and do some cooking together.

William (12). It was found William ate a fairly restricted diet (toast, cheese, waffles, baked beans, mashed potatoes, sausages, sweetcorn and eggs) and was unwilling to eat what the rest of the family ate. Suggestions were to have more protein such as beans or eggs. As he often had colds and sore throats it was thought that his lack of vegetables and fruit had led to a weakened immune system. Ways of eating different fruit and vegetables were discussed, and healthy snacks he could get himself.

Discussion led to the different choices from the school lunch menu. He seemed unwilling to make changes and it was explained that new foods needed to be tried fifteen times before they were accepted.

Handouts about blood sugar balance, a food challenge chart and ways to encourage eating fruit and vegetables were given. An adult multivitamin and mineral supplements were prescribed.

At the second session William had made significant changes, he had tried bananas, yoghurt, peas, chicken, carrots, swede, stuffing, and boiled potatoes. Although he had found it difficult, he had had a lot of support from his family. We discussed healthier choices at school lunch again, and to continue trying proper meat.

Massage

Peter (11). When Peter had a back and face massage, he said he had not liked it. His mother said she would massage him every night. They reported the next week that she had done so. He was more lively at the third session, had a good massage, and mother expressed her surprise because usually he did not like being touched.

Angela (6) happily got on the couch to have a massage, relaxed and went into an altered state. Scores were done and Mum was asked to continue some massage at home. At the second session we discussed the family arguments which had involved Angela, but she had stood up for herself and her mother. They had not done any massage at home as she had had her birthday. Metamorphic technique was shown (a light tapping and stroking of the head, hands and feet) and a handout given.

William (12) did not want to get on the couch; as he was older this was accepted. His mother was given our DVD showing massage techniques and asked to do some at home. William agreed to try feet next time. A flower remedy sheet was given. At the next session they reported no massage had been done. We did a hand massage, which he enjoyed, and progressed to his feet. He was introduced to the idea of saying yes to life and opportunities.

Imagery

Peter (11) was extremely shy, and said as little as possible in a very low voice. So talking was done to the bear. After creating rapport, he was introduced to the idea of being able to move pictures around in our mind. He responded well to this. Eventually he was able to sit up with the bear next to him.

Peter chose an important, unpleasant incident (unknown) for a rewind, to clear emotions from a negative memory, and again he responded well. He then told us about a teacher shouting at pupils which had upset him. He imagined this and was helped to do a 'blow out', a technique to clear an emotional state or habit, sending it behind him forever.

At the next session he relaxed and came out from behind the bear to sit beside it and talk. He was introduced to the set of Babushka dolls, where the second to last doll has an upset face. We explained that sometimes things happen in life, but that you can get over it. He was interested but did not play with it.

Peter was having trouble concentrating at school, letting his mind drift to more interesting thoughts. He was told about hunter gatherers and the farmers, and how hunters notice everything, but he would have to learn to get by when he was with single-minded farmers. Eulers disc was played (as it spins it gets faster and stronger) with Peter hearing several comments about the disk recovering and going better. He then imagined himself doing well at school and saw himself going right through the day feeling good.

The last session was general talking, the story of Chicken Licken and perspective given.

Angela (6). We did a rewind on the dog incident and a metaphoric story about being angry and dealing with anger. Mum was about to go into hospital, so Angela would be staying with her maternal grandmother. With another story, reinforcement was given about it being safe for Mum to go away.

At the second session the bullying incident was explained. She was helped to imagine the bully on a TV screen, with her hair all cut out, and in Mickey Mouse clothes, and Angela laughing at her. She imagined all her school friends laughing and then included all the puppets on her fingers and the cow mooing, all laughing.

Her mother asked for a rewind of the family argument, but it seemed the incident had been handled positively, so it was decided to leave things as they were.

William (12). Again William was generally non-co-operative and did not want to attend. He did not like change and said he was unwilling to try the change in diet. Anger was discussed and where he held it in his body, but he did not appear to be in touch with his feelings. Stein's clenched fist technique was explained as a tool to capture anger in the fist and then letting it go. There was a change in attitude with a toy dog and a magic trick.

At the second session he had been using the fist technique when angry. Homework was discussed and his mother helped him set up a routine, which he said he would do himself. He had created a special place – a secret garden and ski park, with dogs and hamsters running around. He had a problem tree upon which he left his problems. Having discussed the benefits of guided visualisation he imagined perfecting moves on his BMX bike.

Results

Peter (11). Within one session and one week, Peter made eye contact and was laughing, even being a bit cheeky. By the third session his catarrh had gone completely. His score for confidence improved from 0 to 9/10. His mother wrote that he seemed much happier and that it had helped in a time of need.

Angela (6). At the second session, Angela's scores had improved. Anger went from 2 to 10/10, family 4 to 8/10 and confidence from 5 to 7/10. They did not respond to emails for a third session, so presumably were satisfied with the outcome from two sessions.

William (12). Despite being unco-operative and unwilling, William had changed his diet, and came to the second session smiling. At the second session after one week, he scored willingness to help from 1 to 7/10 and friendly from 2 to 5/10. Although three sessions are generally suggested, his mother emailed to say 'he was doing great, eating healthily, and was calmer and happier. He enjoyed massages, and school, and was not in so much trouble. He thought about things before acting and all the family could see the good side to him now – happy, funny, loving, kind, helpful and caring. They were going out together more (previously it was always a battle) and they had seen a Michael Jackson film, which had been the best time ever. They played games in the evening and he was interested in all sorts of things. 'It's great and we cannot thank you and the staff enough for helping him find his confidence and self esteem that he was lacking.'

Parent's letter after treatment for lack of confidence

Dear Clover House,

I write with regard to Gary and his progress. When we brought him to Clover House he was a desperately sad young boy who was experiencing serious problems with friendships, which were having a debilitating effect on the rest of his life. For him and for us it was a very unhappy time.

Gary eventually made the decision to withdraw from the friends he had known from childhood, and during the summer break from school, did not see anyone. Despite our misgivings about this decision, Gary became less anxious.

On returning to school he gradually made new friends, and in the past six months there has been a clear change in his demeanour and attitude. Being 15 years old, he naturally still suffers from the usual bouts of incoherence and being stroppy, but I am delighted to report that he is like a new person and fun to be with and around.

This episode, although very unpleasant for him and us, and the manner in which he has handled it, has given him much self belief and self confidence.

We took on board the advice given as regards to diet and continue with many of the suggestions made, and I also give him a back massage from time to time, which he loves. Sadly I still haven't managed to get him to give me one!

My husband and I would like to take this opportunity to thank you all for the part you played in helping Gary.

Chapter 17

Constipation

All the children who came to Clover House for constipation for two or more sessions improved. The average score at commencement was 1.5/10 and improving to 9/10 at the end, within an average of four sessions

The Problems

Bella aged 2 had been suffering for two months and as well as experiencing sore anal fissures and pain, she was experiencing some psychological problems, frightened to go to the toilet, with tears and screaming. She had been prescribed suppositories and laxatives.

Kate aged 4 had been suffering severely for a year, avoiding going to the toilet. Mum wrote that she 'stops herself going with all her might and says she is frightened to go because it will hurt'. When she needed to go she was miserable and 'poorly' for up to five days, lying down, and would not get up and walk, and the family had stopped going out. She had been on two different laxatives for a year. They had been to a health visitor, the doctor, a hospital consultant and registrar, and the Accident & Emergency Department.

Sara age 2.5 had been suffering for three months, distressed and complaining of a 'sore bottom', and would go several days without going to the toilet. Her parents were becoming increasingly anxious. They had been giving her three different laxatives, but as Mum said, 'with no discernible improvement'.

Nutrition

Bella (2) was asked to reduce sugary foods, and the family was given ideas for healthier snacks and treats, and asked to reduce her milk intake to half over the next week and replace it with soya, rice, oats or goat's milk. It was also suggested they buy a new beaker to make the new drinks special.

Other advice included giving diluted apple and prune juice, chamomile tea and water to drink (four cups a day); to have soaked cracked linseeds every day (as a source of soluble fibre) and fibrous fruits and vegetables during the day. An Epsom salts bath at night with lavender was suggested to help restful sleep, and they were given a summary nutrition sheet and constipation handout together with a supplement of acidophilus to help Bella's immune system, and calendula cream for her anal fissures.

Kate (4). Mum was given various suggestions to help soften stools and suggestions to change the diet and boost the immune system. Professionally prescribed children's vitamin and mineral supplements were given. Also advice to gradually change from cow's milk to goat's milk, and a gradual removal of laxatives.

Sara (2.5) had already been diagnosed with lactose intolerance after breast feeding and was using soya milk.

However goat's milk was suggested as it is nearer human milk, and nutrients were prescribed. The family was asked to introduce foods with higher water content such as strawberries and cucumber. Reassurance was given on continuing to change the diet.

Massage

Bella (2). Bella's mother had previously received reflexology and shiatsu herself, and experienced their benefits. She was shown how to do Bella's feet, especially in the middle of the sole which corresponds to the colon. At the second session Mum reported doing all her homework.

Kate (4). Kate's mother was shown how to rub Kate's tummy and to press and circle the corresponding reflexology points on the soles of the feet. Kate was happy and enthusiastic and Mum practiced while Kate was on the couch.

Sara (2.5). Sara willingly got on the couch for us to show Mum tummy and foot massage. Mum was given some massage oils (grape seed and lavender) to use every day at home. Mum reported Sara passed a motion the next day after her session, and that she often asked for her bottom to be massaged for relief.

Imagery

Bella (2) played with toys at her first session, being rather shy, so work was done with Mum clearing some traumatic experiences that were still affecting her.

At the second session Mum was asked if she had a problem that was unresolved, and she chose her daughter's constipation. She was asked to think about something she enjoyed doing and was good at, and then to think about the problem. These two states were 'anchored' with a word and a touch, and then 'collapsed', i.e. interchanged. Mum later reported she felt more confident in dealing with things.

Kate (4). We felt it was important not to put Kate under any pressure because she had been made to 'go' at day nursery, which had upset her. But Kate had fun at her sessions and responded delightedly.

Imagery was used to change her perception of the toilet experience and in the first session there was much use made of three cuddly toys which she had brought along, one of which developed a need to go to the loo.

Kate recounted having been to the cinema the previous day to see a film about Tarzan, and this was used to create a story involving a six-year-old Tarzan who invented the first flushing lavatory and thereby solved his own toilet problem. (The next day Kate told her nursery that Tarzan invented the toilet.)

Sara (2.5). Again because of her tender age, it was decided to work more with Mum, to reduce her anxiety with explanations and reassurance, thereby taking the pressure off Sara 'to perform'. She had three sessions which involved some simple allegorical story-telling and confidence boosting.

Results

Bella (2). After one session they scored improvement from 1/10 to 7/10 and Mum shed tears of gratitude. She reported that Bella was having a bowel movement at least once a day and had not been getting upset. In a lovely long thank you letter Mum wrote that 'Clover House is a sanctuary, a place of healing with kind staff that make you feel supported and positive about the steps you are about to take on the road to recovery.' They attended for two sessions.

Kate (4). Eleven days after she first came to Clover House, Kate's problem was solved, compared to a whole (unsuccessful) year of conventional methods. After one session they reported improvement. At the final third session scores improved from 1/10 to 9/10, and after a month Mum reported Kate was off medication and 'going' regularly. After three months Mum said everything was normal. She wrote 'It has been an amazing experience and I can't thank everyone at Clover House enough.'

Sara (2.5) The main thrust was to reduce Sara's stress and make changes to her diet; this helped alleviate her parents' anxiety. Dad had been very sceptical! By the third session Sara was asking to go to the toilet (previously she wouldn't even refer to it). By the final session she had no tummy pain and her bowel problem was resolved. They scored improvement from 2 to 8.5/10.

Parent's Letter after treatment for Constipation
Dear Clover House,

Kate's problem began about a year before we contacted Clover House. Just after her third birthday and she had been potty trained, she began having problems going to the toilet. She had always been a bit constipated but her stools became very large and it had hurt her to go.

Her fear just got worse and she would always stop herself from going, sometimes for 3–5 days. Every time she got the urge she would hold it in with all her might. Eventually she would have no choice but to go. It was quite a traumatic experience for her but afterwards she became a totally different person, back to normal. Kate would then be OK for a couple of days and then it would start all over again.

The days when she wanted to go would be awful, sometimes I would be in despair and not know what to do for the best. She would often just spend the day lying down, drinking milk and feeling poorly. We would spend days just trying to get her to eat high fibre foods, taking her medicine and sitting on the toilet. To go out when she was poorly was very trying. She would constantly have to stop walking or whatever she was doing to stop herself from going to the toilet. I felt as if everybody was staring and wondering what was wrong with her. Sometimes we would just end up going home again. Often we would decide not to go somewhere unless it was essential.

After a month or so of this first occurring I mentioned it to my health visitor. She said it was a common problem and suggested lots of high fibre food and doing a star chart with rewards for sitting on the potty and going. She then suggested a visit to Kate's GP. The GP assured me it was a very common problem and said the same as the health visitor except she thought a laxative should be taken, this would soften the stools and give Kate no choice but to go. It was hard work trying constantly to get her to eat certain foods, take her medicine and sit on the potty. However, it didn't seem to matter how much medicine or fibre she took, it didn't have much effect.

I kept returning to the GP as the problem didn't resolve itself and I didn't know what else to do. She suggested giving senna as well as the laxative. She said it would take time but we would get on top of the problem eventually. I asked if there were any self-help groups or alternatives as it would have helped if I could have spoken to someone with similar problems. I rang the organisation that deals with bed wetting. They were very sympathetic and sent me a booklet which gave me some reassurance that the problem was as we saw it and not a more serious physical problem. I also rang Link a Parent, they didn't seem to have anyone I could talk to with similar problems and gave me the impression they dealt with more serious problems.

There were days when Kate felt really poorly and on one occasion her nursery even suggested I take her to A & E. One doctor told me if she ate a Weetabix a day she would not have a problem.

Eventually after about six months Kate's GP said she would refer her to the Children's Hospital. She said not to expect an immediate result as it was going to take several visits. She said sometimes children are taken in overnight to be cleaned out and start again. This frightened me, I asked if she could see a psychologist as the problem seemed to be a mental one. She said they may well refer Kate to a psychologist.

After about a month we were given an appointment. We were to see a consultant specialising in children's bowel problems. Initially we saw the senior registrar who was very sympathetic and said it was a very common problem. The advice was the same diet, star charts, medicine and regular sitting on the toilet. He said Kate had lost her natural ability to go and had to re-learn this. He also increased the amount of medicine and said GPs always under-prescribed for children.

On the second visit we saw the consultant and she re-assured me there wasn't anything physically wrong with Kate. She gave the same advice as before but also used bullying tactics. She told me to clear my kitchen cupboards and only have healthy high fibre foods and said if the parents ate healthily then her workload would be greatly reduced. I had been trying really hard to ensure Kate ate a lot of high fibre foods but was made to feel very inadequate. At no point was the mental aspect addressed.

After about a year things really came to a head one weekend which Kate was spending with her grandparents. My dad got really upset and said I must return to the hospital and insist they do something as it wasn't fair for Kate to feel so poorly all the time. I had done all I could to the best of my ability, everything the medics had suggested. I thought I should explore alternatives. I looked through Yellow Pages and came upon Clover House.

I gave them a ring and had a conversation with a lovely man who thought he could help Kate. He sent a video which we watched and I thought this makes so much sense what they are talking about but how can it really work. I was also a little apprehensive that they dealt with children with more serious problems. Although this problem was very serious to us it wasn't really recognised as such by the medical profession. Anyway I decided we would visit and I would keep an open mind as I was willing to give anything a go.

At our first visit everybody was really friendly and we mainly just chatted, getting to know each other. Kate was very shy so not too much could be done (or so I thought).

Anyway when we left I realised the first visit had made an enormous impact on Kate. She talked about the magic man and how he was going to send magic to her at home to help her go to the toilet. Amazingly Kate started sitting on her potty and going of her own accord. She still got frightened at first but gradually the fear disappeared.

Kate was looking forward to her second visit. The nutritionist gave some advice on her diet and suggested it was the milk in her diet that was causing a lot of the constipation and making her stools bulky. We put her on goat's milk. As she gradually felt better her milk intake reduced and she started eating more. She now only has milk to go to bed. We also found the massage of her tummy and feet particularly beneficial and Kate enjoys this very much. I found that if she needed to go, a little massage would often do the trick.

I gradually started to reduce Kate's medication and she was totally off all medicine after a month. She was going regularly of her own accord but her stools were still large. Now after three months I would say her stools are normal as the nutritionist predicted.

It has been an amazing experience and I can't thank everyone at Clover House enough, they are all lovely people. When I look back over the past year, there were times when it was a nightmare and I am just thankful I discovered Clover House. I wish somebody had told me about its existence months ago.

Kate's Mum.

Chapter 18

Depression

All children who came to Clover House suffering from low moods or depression improved substantially. The average score at commencement was 1.5/10 and improved to 8/10 in an average of four sessions.

The Problems

Molly aged 14 came with four symptoms: depression, low self esteem, eating problems and self harm. Her mother and father had been concerned for six months previously, and her friends had been so worried they had consulted her parents.

Alan aged 14. Mum wrote that the family had hit a low that could not be put into words. Alan had been in trouble with the police and had been expelled from school. Alan said he was depressed and had no motivation, could not sleep and watched films until late at night, but could not relax.

Toni aged 16. Mum wrote that her daughter had depression, was angry a lot of the time, made herself vomit after meals, had poor self esteem, and felt life was not worth living, with nothing to look forward to – not a happy girl.

Toni's parents had taken her to a child psychologist at age 11, diagnosed with attention deficit hyperactivity disorder (ADHD) and prescribed the drug Ritalin since age 13, but the side effects had been detrimental. She had also been to a child and adolescent unit, but refused to co-operate or open up.

Nutrition

Molly (14) was tearful throughout her first session (as were Mum and Dad), and more emotional when she was asked to eat different foods. Mum and Dad were keen to help and said they would try to get her to follow our recommendations. Molly was a vegetarian and was asked to increase her protein, such as quorn, tofu and egg white omelettes, to supply more energy.

She was prescribed rhodiola for stress and later a multivitamin and linseed oil for essential fats as she did not want to take fish oils. She was encouraged to try porridge or muesli with seeds and chopped fruit. Explanations were given of the importance of combining sources of vegetarian protein to get the full complement of amino acids and she was given a list. As osteoporosis ran in the family, the need to eat dark green leafy vegetables was strongly emphasised.

Alan (13) was interested in nutrition (he wanted to be a scientist), and listened to the explanation of how good food and supplements could help his depression, anger and concentration. His homework was to get 14 stars for eating more fruit and vegetables, and drink more water. He was prescribed a Vitamin B complex and magnesium.

Toni (16) received over twelve suggestions, including trying fruit juices, to increase 'B' foods (brown bread, brown rice and brown pasta), drink 1.5 litres of water a day, and have at least two apples, a banana and other fruit every day, and to have oily fish at least twice a week. The only tinned foods were to be oily fish and low-sugar baked beans. She should have three portions of nuts and seeds a week, and increase iron-rich foods (watercress, dried raisins, and red meat) and a B complex supplement was prescribed. A chromium supplement was suggested to help combat chocolate cravings, and magnesium was prescribed for relaxation and to help memory recall for her exams.

Massage

Molly (14) did not make eye contact or talk during our first session, just making sounds to answer questions. Dad left the room so that Mum could learn some massage, but she was nervous of hurting her and ended up tickling her. However it was suggested that laughter was good medicine.

At her second session, Molly was crying, but lay down on the couch for some head massage, and at the third session made up her own secret prescription of flower remedies. She enjoyed talking about a book she had borrowed about ancient wisdoms, and about her plans for the future.

Alan (13). After having a foot massage it was noted Alan visibly relaxed, had less twitching and seemed calmer. Mum practised the massage techniques in order to continue at home. It was suggested that Alan try the gym to help increase his endorphins and self esteem.

Toni (16) had massage with Mum watching so she could carry on at home. Toni talked about going to college.

Imagery

Molly (14) did not speak at her first session, but she listened to general chat about thoughts and images, how to change things and what could be done. Mum suggested she could have the next session on her own, and Molly was able to externalise some of her 'bad ' feelings. A 'rewind' (to clear the emotional element of a memory) was done on an undisclosed incident that had upset her, and completed this with a 'blow out' (to clear a habit). Work was done on helping Molly eat in public which was a problem for her. Help was given for coping better generally.

Alan (13) said he hated being grounded by his parents, which made him angry and unhappy. He did two 'rewinds' on incidents when he was aged 5 at school, and on two recent groundings. He perked up when talk got round to dealing with dares. His friends were older than him and egged him on, but then he got the blame. He was asked what kind of boys allow someone three years younger to lead them? He replied 'Losers.'

Having been in trouble for being fifteen minutes late getting back home, at the next session we tried to 'reframe' and change his thinking. He said the word 'try' which was changed to 'to do' in his head. He was told a story about a fourteen-year-old wearing an earring and how a £5 earring could rob you of a future.

Toni (16) did lots of work with imagery including clearing her first bullying experience. She was shown how to change images in order to disassociate them, and to improve her recall of good memories and reduce bad memories. She remembered a time when she helped someone and went back in the past to help the younger Toni, using all her resources as she grew up. Toni called herself 'stupid' and was helped to change this to 'Oh dear, that's not usual for me. What can I do to make it better next time?' She imagined herself making a mistake as her new self. One last issue was about doing the ironing – to use a strategy of pleasure principle – every item earned a word of praise and each item meant she was closer to finishing the job. A finished job looked really good and deserved even more praise.

The Results

Molly (14). By the third session Molly was cheerful (having previously been tearful) and her clothes were more colourful. She changed to being happy to talk about foods, listened to suggestions, and increased her range of foods. Her scores improved for overall happiness from 2/10 to 7/10.

Alan (13). Because he lived several counties away, Alan attended for just two sessions. His scores improved on being happier from 1 to 7/10 within one week and sleep from 2 to 6/10. Mum wrote six months later to say that Alan was at a new school and doing really well. He had received a national award for a maths test. Mum said four family members had benefitted. She liked the fact that the whole person was dealt with from diet to relaxation and to talking about problems, and scored us 10/10 on service and success on her child's condition.

Toni (16). After four weekly sessions, scores improved from 4, 5 and 7 to 8/10 for being happy. Two years later

Mum confirmed she had a happier daughter, and she was training at beauty college. Apparently whenever she passed Clover House she would often comment, 'How lovely it would be to work there.'

Parent's Letter after treatment for Depression

Dear Clover House,

It seems strange to be putting our experiences down on paper, to think how this all started and how our lives have changed for the better. So here goes!

Back in July of last year I happened to pick up a leaflet telling me all about Clover House. I read it and thought I'll give them a ring sometime and see if they can help James, our 10-year-old son.

James has always had problems at school but gradually these problems were manifesting into behavioural problems and emotionally James was a wreck, it was if he was suffering from a form of depression. He has never really enjoyed school, but knew he had to go so rarely complained.

During the month of July we had meetings with the school and decided to try to get James extra help by getting a statement for September; this was in place for his final year in primary school!

James was not keen to take on board Clover House and took some persuading to even walk through the door, but I felt it was our only chance of some sanity in our lives. James was sulky, moody, and generally a very unhappy little boy.

When we arrived, we were introduced to the team. James spent the first hour trying everything he could to avoid eye contact, and trying to climb inside my back. He was determined not to co-operate, he felt threatened by all the people.

He was shown some magic tricks and was then left to calm down and regain his composure. After a few minutes, curiosity got the better of him because he wanted to see inside the magic room. We both went in and gradually James opened up a bit. We then saw the nutritionist who advised me to cut out all dairy produce, squashes, coke, etc., and avoid as many foods containing preservatives as possible. (That meant me learning to cook again!)

I did this with a vengeance: orange juice is now in the cupboard, dairy-free margarine, goat's milk, and organic produce like I can't imagine!

Then onto the massage therapist who encourages both mum and dad to gently massage their child, showing you a few strokes to encourage you to get in touch with your child (to bond). Again I took this on with a vengeance, James loves it, and has always asked to have a massage right from the beginning. I have realised a long-term goal of becoming a therapist and started a massage course to help James, the family, myself and others.

Sorry! Back to James. After 10 days of cutting out certain foods, James was a changed boy, loving, happy and not as angry with everybody. Unfortunately we went on holiday, (10 days after we first started at Clover House). Within that two-week period James's personality started to change back – the anger, the sulks, everything we had been trying so hard to change. This is what happens when we went all inclusive, he thought he could have fizzy drinks, foods with preservatives, etc.

Within three days of coming back off holiday and onto dairy free, no fizzy drinks, he was changing back again to the happy little boy I enjoyed having around.

Before this James was having so many detentions for not

behaving it was laughable, but since September he has only had two, and is coping with school, and life in general. He is achieving in all areas, is growing in confidence, and is starting to enjoy (dare I say it) school. James still has his moments but in general he likes himself when he is happy and is aware when he has drunk or eaten something he knows is not good for him.

I hope James can carry this newfound confidence into his new school in September, and can fly through his teens without too many hurdles. I hope this letter is of some help, I realise I have shortened the sequence of events, but that does not in any way detract from the gratitude my husband and I have for all of you and the work you do for all the children and families you see. All I can say to Clover House is a very big thank you for giving us back our little boy, who is loving, smiling and enjoying life, not the depressed little boy you saw last July.

James's Mum.

Chapter 19

Dyslexia

All the children who came to Clover House with dyslexia came with an average of four or five symptoms. These included low self esteem, anxiety, low mood, anger and lack of confidence. Their average scores at commencement were 2.6/10 and improved to 7/10 within an average of 3.6 sessions.

The Problems

Rachael aged 7 came with a lengthy report from an Educational Psychologist. Her mother, a teacher, was worried about her daughter's lack of confidence, concentration, writing, innumeracy and her anxiety. At her first session Rachael said she was worried about people, and that if she talked too much she could not get her words out and they got all mixed up.

Wendy aged 16 had been diagnosed dyslexic at the age of 10. She had low self esteem, depressed mood, relationship difficulties, weight loss and anger. She disclosed she made herself sick after meals when stressed, and her menstrual cycle had stopped.

Joseph aged 12 was diagnosed dyslexic at the age of 9 and was suffering from low mood, low energy, low appetite, and a lack of motivation. Mum reported that he struggled with homework and lost concentration quickly, and easily became confused.

Nutrition

Rachael (7) was enthralled by the magic book, and was reassured that changing to different foods could help her stop worrying. The therapist 'talked' to her imaginary friend about helping Rachael, and suggested reading slowly to her imaginary friends in front of a mirror. Supplements of a liquid multivitamin and eskimo oils were prescribed.

Advice included having more energy-sustaining foods throughout the day, especially in the afternoon, and substantial snacks, i.e. banana, homemade fruitcake or flapjack. We recommended she change her berry juice to apple juice (less sugar), preferably watered down. With her high salt diet recorded, to have a minimum of six glasses/1.5 litres of water a day to stay hydrated and help brain function.

Wendy (16). We had an in-depth discussion about foods and how the body worked regarding weight gain. Although she had been vegetarian since the age of 5, she had become anaemic, and now ate meat and fish. She was asked to keep a diary of her periods, and a food diary. B complex vitamins, magnesium and supplements were given. Wendy and her mother had lots of handouts, and asked lots of questions.

Further motivation was given to improve diet and to make sure she ate snacks and fruit regularly. Later from the diary it was found she was still eating junk food and lots of fizzy drinks, so emphasis was made on no fizzy drinks, alcohol, coffee or citrus fruit or just cereal for breakfast. After one month she wanted to come back to Clover House for support.

Mum asked how much alcohol she could have, and was told none! One month of chromium supplements was given. At the eighth session she reported suffering tummy aches, migraines and being afraid to sleep in the dark, and feeling depressed. Mum reported she was missing meals. She was given further B complex and magnesium and we suggested having smoothies. She also reported not getting on with her twin sisters. At the tenth session she asked for a sample menu of good foods.

Joseph (12) Mum reported that she was strict with food and was herself anxious about foods, so that Joseph's anxiety might have come from her. It was suggested that the whole family should eat more brown bread and brown foods for vitamin B. A star chart was suggested to improve eating, aiming to achieve 40 stars, with two stars for eating lunch. It was advised that someone be with Joseph at school to see that he ate his food. Lunchtime menu suggestions were given.

Massage

Rachael (7). Mum reported they already did what they called 'scratch and tickle' at home. Mum watched a massage routine and was asked to do some every night before sleep. A flower remedy was chosen which included aspen for fears and worries, clematis for day dreaming, larch for lack of confidence, red chestnut for over-anxiety and concern, and wild rose for apathy. Advice was given about being a big sister.

Wendy (16). A flower remedy was prepared for use at home. Some foot massage was explained (Dad already did massage), and general discussion led to Wendy saying she felt excluded in the family. Some more massage was done at the next session. Mum did Reiki healing, but not much homework had been done due to time issues. Wendy asked for reflexology. Another flower remedy was prepared for confidence.

Six months later Wendy returned feeling low, and we discussed with Mum the pressures on teenagers, especially with Wendy doing drama at college, the competitiveness, performing and the feelings of anti-climax on finishing a performance. A new flower remedy was completed. We suggested that her own ironing should be kept in her room, to be done when she can.

At a further session, we encouraged Wendy to think about the idea that at 17 she could begin to be responsible for her own life and choices, and that other people could not do it for her.

Joseph (12). It was reported Joseph already had massage at home, so we suggested it was done more regularly.

Imagery

Rachael (7) identified with the Babushka dolls sequence where the face of the second-to-last doll has an upset face, and the story that things can go wrong sometimes but you can get over it. Mum reported that Rachael panicked with numbers, but letters were alright, so Rachael was asked to write a list starting with A and putting 1 next to it, then B with 2, and so on. She saw the joke and wrote 211 and said Baa.

She took over and wrote C followed by 3, but the 3 was a mirror image. She was given a mirror idea – to think of the number in her mind and reflect it in a mirror. She then wrote 3 correctly. This was repeated with number 4, and again thinking of it in a mirror.

At the second session, Rachael revealed a fear of dogs, so we introduced her to the 'anchors' technique, where a state (i.e. fear) is connected to the body, and a corresponding good state was set up for dogs and enjoyment of drawing. The anchors were 'collapsed' (resulting in the negative state clearing) which left her giggling and relaxed.

Rachael reported she was better with numbers but they still frightened her. When asked what colours they were, letters were red, words were red/blue and numbers were purple. She was asked to turn the numbers to green.

At the third session Mum and Rachael got involved with stories about brave people. Rachael was shown how to do a 'golden circle' by imagining three different school friends who were confident, standing in there, being confident, one after the other. We then put the three inside a circle, coming together as one very confident girl. Rachael stepped into the circle and into the confidence. She liked this and practised on her own. The image of a mountain lioness protecting her cubs was installed to help with more confidence.

Wendy (16). At her initial session Wendy wanted different goals to her mother, so a compromise was reached. Seeing her on her own, she said she felt left out because Mum had Dad and her twin sisters had each other. 'I am on my own'. So a 'rewind' (a technique to clear the emotional element of a memory) was done on a film of Wendy as an only child, and the arrival of the twins. This was done twice. 'Reframing' of twins in general was done and how twins find it difficult to separate later in life. Wendy had difficulty accessing good memories of times she succeeded under stress, so imagery was used to change the structure of good/bad memories. Then an imagery technique was done to push bad memories into the background and good memories to the foreground. Also anchors were established for handling stress well as opposed to handling it badly. These anchors were collapsed and tested and Wendy had difficulty accessing 'handling badly' afterwards.

At the next session she said she was behind on college work and all her written assignments. She explained she had difficulty putting words together and could not spell very well. When tested she started by visualising words when spelling them, but then lost concentration. Wendy was helped to see letters more clearly by spelling words backwards, using colour and strategies such as splitting a word for spelling. Later a 'car wash' technique (imagining spraying with a car wash of rainbow loving colours) was used for her sisters.

We then addressed the problem of prioritising work. She went through imagining writing her autobiography and seeing herself through the eyes of someone who loved her. Further work was done on audition nerves with a 'blow out' technique for banishing negative habits, which was totally successful. Lastly work was done on sleeping without the light on. Also on changing criticism to feedback, then watching herself deal with feedback in a new way where criticism was reframed as information.

Joseph (12). Work was done on future planning and thinking ahead. Also an imagery with Joseph picturing himself succeeding in the future. Suggestions were made to switch homework tasks every fifteen minutes and to spend allocated time doing homework only.

The Results

Rachael (7). Mum reported that massage 'had been really good'. At the third session it was reported that Rachael was no longer afraid of dogs. Three months later scores had improved: anxiety from 5 to 7/10, numbers from 2 to 5/10 and confidence from 5 to 7/10 . Mum wrote, 'Coming to Clover House gave us dedicated time to consider her worries and strategies for future use. She thoroughly enjoyed the sessions, feeling pampered and cared for at each visit.'

Wendy (16). By the fourth session Wendy said she felt great, but still wanted support. By the seventh session she said her weight was no longer an issue and she accepted she was growing into a woman.

There was a blip six months later so she had several more sessions. She later sent a thank you card in which she wrote, 'Thank you for helping me through a hard stage in my life, lots of love.' Mum wrote, 'Thank you all for everything, it's been great.' They scored motivation improved from 2 to 8/10, general wellbeing 4 to 9/10, anger from 3 to 9/10 and thinking ahead from 2 to 9/10.

Joseph (12). At the second session, one week after the first, Mum said food was no longer a problem as she was taking more control. Joseph said he was fine. They scored anxious improved from 1 to 5/10, decisive about food from 1 to 8/10, self esteem from 1 to 5/10 and being more decisive from 3 to 6/10.

Chapter 20

Eczema

The majority of the children who came to Clover House for eczema, substantially improved after two or three sessions, clearing their skin of sores, scabs, itching, and greatly improved sleep. The average score for eczema was 3/10 at commencement, improved to 8.2/10 within an average of three sessions.

The Problems

Tilly aged 5 had been suffering with eczema since she was 18 months old. She was under the paediatrician and dermatologist at hospital. She was constantly scratching and had sores on her whole body. She had to be creamed and bandaged up every night. They had tried sedatives, but she was still waking her mother with the distress of itching, and bandages coming loose. She had also developed anxieties about using the cream, of flies and dirt, and of people talking or laughing about her. Her mother was unable to take her out. They scored eczema problems 0/10.

Mary aged 4 had had eczema since a year old, was red and sore all over her body and had to use wet bandages and creams. She was tired because of broken sleep. Pre-school reported she was becoming withdrawn, not participating and not talking to the staff. Mum also reported her being clingy, having toilet accidents and was back in nappies. She was scared of dreams and going to sleep, and of being alone in her room. Mum was anxious about Mary's condition and felt she would not be able to start school unless there was some improvement. They scored eczema at 1/10.

Oliver aged 4 had had eczema from birth (although it had cleared for a while between ages 1 and 2). They had steroids, emollients and bandages, and had tried homeopathy. Mum had asked the GP for an allergy test but he said Oliver really needed more steroid cream. They scored eczema at 4/10.

Nutrition

Tilly (5). We suggested Tilly should avoid all food triggers for eczema – dairy foods, eggs, peanuts, tomatoes, chocolate, soya and citrus fruits. Her diet was found to be high in dairy foods, particularly as she craved cheese, with a lot of high-sugar snacks. Mum thought it would be manageable to change the cheese to buffalo mozzarella, goat's cheese and feta. She was also asked to increase Tilly's intake of foods that contain the flavanoid quercetin (onions, apples, pears). Advice included increasing high anti-oxidant and anti-inflamatory foods such as berries, broccoli and oily fish and to reduce her sugar intake.

To help her sleep we suggested she had Epsom salts in her bedtime bath, and put some oats into a sock, allowing the oats to hydrate and rub the sock on her skin for soothing. Mum was given an eczema, blood sugar and healthy diet handouts, plus children's chewable multivitamin and minerals, junior EPA oil tablets and lactobacillus supplements, to increase nutrients and help gut flora.

Various topical treatments were suggested including Vitamins E and A creams, aloe vera extract and bio-oil to prevent skin scarring.

Mary (4). Mum agreed to try avoiding citrus fruit juices in case they were a problem and to reduce sugar. She was given a summary sheet, an eczema handout, and ways to encourage eating fruit and vegetables.

At the second session Mum had asked for a food intolerance test and Mary was found to be intolerant of many foods. Food alternatives were discussed, and handouts on food intolerances, digestion and leaky gut were given. It was explained that even a small amount of an intolerant food can produce strong reactions. However Mum was reluctant to remove wheat and yeast from her diet. We gave her suggestions of non-toast ideas for breakfast and recipes for non-wheat and non-yeast bread, as Dad made bread at home.

Supplements were suggested: probiotic, a junior multivitamin, digestive enzymes and acidophilus. At the third session it was emphasised that Mary needed to take all her supplements to see an improvement.

Oliver (4). We suggested Oliver would benefit from eating more oily fish, oils, nuts and seeds. Further suggestions were to reduce dairy products, red meat, sugar, fried and processed foods which are inflammatory, and to increase his intake of fruit and vegetables as they are alkalising on the body. Mum was later asked to eliminate all dairy from Oliver's diet for one month and she was given good alternative sources of calcium. At a further session it was reported that Oliver loved rice milk.

Mum was advised about what to avoid in processed foods, e.g. whey powder and sodium caseinate, and an explanation of how Oliver's gut lining was probably leaky (due to dairy intolerance) and that it would heal gradually as the irritation of dairy foods subsided. It was also suggested that he took a digestive enzyme to reduce inflammation, and a supplement to help heal his gut. Junior Digestaid was prescribed.

Massage
Tilly (5) was too distressed with itching and scratching (which increased with new situations and people) to have any massage. Mum was shown some reflexology and it was noted that everyone gradually relaxed. As Mum had to smother Tilly in cream every night, we suggested she apply it as a massage, caringly and soothingly. At the second session Mum was able to see and learn some massage techniques. Handouts of deep breathing techniques, and massage were given with a relaxation CD. Another 'metamorphic technique' was shown, tapping and stroking on the head, hands and feet.

Mary (4). We explained to Mary's mother how to give some massage, and gave her a flower remedy sheet. As they did not have time at the second session they were given one of our DVDs which contains a massage sequence to watch. At the third session we gave Mary's brother a massage while Mary was drawing, which pleased Mum as this was the first time she had sat down to draw for ages.

Oliver (4) was too busy having fun to come in and have some massage, but eventually agreed to sit on Mum's lap and have his back rubbed. Mum thought he would be better having a massage at home when he was tired and ready for bed. Later she reported that Oliver had massage every night since his first session and loved it, and tells her not to miss anything. We suggested she fill a hot water bottle with very cold water to use at night to stop the itching, and try dead sea salts in the bath.

Imagery

Tilly (5) had fun playing on the swing in the Clover House garden, but when she came in she spotted a fly which sent her into a panic attack. So we went back into the garden, where she was distracted by a magic trick (£1 coin from behind her ear). Negative emotional effects were neutralised. Rapport was established with her bringing her favourite teddy and meeting the therapists old toy, Monk.

A further session was used to practise 'going floppy' and for Tilly to practise this at bedtimes with Mum's help. Relaxation would help Tilly's anxieties about flies and dirt.

Oliver (4) was shy, but was shown the toy boxes and played while Mum did a 'rewind', a technique to clear the emotional element of a memory and detach memories on her childbirth experience.

Magic was used with Oliver and then he was shown and told the story of the Babushka dolls who was very happy but suddenly became upset with an upset face, but she learnt to deal with it and regained her happiness.

At the next session Oliver came with his sister and they wanted to play with the toys, but eventually he paid enough attention to try techniques for replacing feeling itchy to feeling comfortable – fleetingly.

Oliver still did not want to talk at his third session, and wanted to play with the yoyo. So it was hidden and a bargain was made that if he sat and talked for a couple of minutes the yoyo would be magic and come back. He was asked to remember a favourite TV programme, and learned how to make this more and more realistic until he laughed and enjoyed it, and he was asked to imagine calmer things. The yoyo reappeared from behind his ear.

Results:

Tilly (5). Mum was really pleased after three sessions. They scored eczema improved from 0 to 6/10. Her face had completely cleared, and considering it had been all over her body, there was now just some on her hands and feet. Her sleeping had improved to 10/10.

Mary (4). Mum was delighted and could see her daughter was happier, and was relieved that they were on track for her to start primary school. They scored eczema improved from 1 to 8/10 within three sessions over one month.

Oliver (4). Mum scored eczema at 4/10 at his first session, two weeks later improved to 7/10 and three months later at 8/10.

Parent's Letter after treatment for Eczema
Dear Clover House,

I contacted Clover House in July 2013 because I was at breaking point with my 5-year-old daughter. Tilly has suffered from eczema since she was about 18 months old, over the years not only was the eczema getting considerably worse, but she was starting to develop strange behavioural problems.

Tilly was about 3 when I started to notice if I took her anywhere she was extremely worried and almost feared anything dirty, she wouldn't sit on chairs or walk on floors if they had any sort of mark on them. She wouldn't leave me to go off and play with friends or her cousins, she would just sit on my lap, cry and itch hysterically. This would also happen if I took her anywhere out of her comfort zone.

Sleeping then became an issue because she would be crying all night because of skin or 'bits' in her bed caused by her itching so much! In April the fear changed from dirt to flies or any sort of bugs, but I still got the same reaction. I was at the point I felt we couldn't go anywhere because I knew Tilly wouldn't enjoy herself, and might even cause herself harm. I felt on edge as I knew no way of trying to calm her down.

Finally in January 2013 after many years of trying, Tilly was referred to a dermatologist in the Royal United Hospital, Bath. While they have done a lot to help her regarding her skin such as wet bandages and a course of UVB light treatment, no one seemed to understand my concern about Tilly's psychological issues that came along side the eczema.

After my first visit [to Clover House], I was told 99% of eczema is caused by an intolerance to dairy, tomatoes and citrus so these should be cut out of Tilly's diet. This had never been mentioned to me before by a doctor.

Clover House therapists said she should also be shown lots of relaxing massage techniques to keep her calm. Both of which has worked wonders and the eczema is 80% better.

Our first visit with the imagery didn't go so well because as soon as we entered the room so did a fly, causing her to act hysterically again. In a way I was glad because he got to see exactly what I was talking about and I was so relieved to receive a phone call from him that evening expressing his concerns and agreeing this couldn't go on!!

The second time we came to Clover House Tilly warmed to the imagery therapist straight away which was very unlike her and he began to work his magic. After three months of seeing him I am overjoyed to have my happy little girl back! No medication and Tilly is a different child! She has no worries about dirt, she plays happily, enjoys school a lot more and I can take her where ever with not one worry about how she will be!! Her fear of flies has also dramatically reduced.

I cannot thank Clover House enough for everything they have done, such a friendly place full of smiling staff! Tilly and I will always be eternally grateful to them as we now have our lives back and can enjoy every day. So once again a HUGE thank you.

Chapter 21

Food Phobias

The average commencement score for food phobias was 2.6/10 and within three sessions finished at 8.25/10. All children had overcome their food phobias and had started eating normally.

The Problems

John aged 9. John's mother was a nurse and wrote that she believed John had a food phobia, which stemmed from an early age. He used to vomit and could not tolerate lumpy foods when weaned, and grew up eating sandwiches and cake only. He was frightened to try any foods, and was sometimes sick at the thought of eating food.

Charlie aged 10. Charlie's mother found us on the internet and wrote that Charlie got very stressed when confronted with foods he did not like, and had a very limited range of foods – no meat or potatoes. It was beginning to impact on his social life. Charlie had had reflux as a baby, and they had been through the child and adolescent mental health service, and had been told to back off and he would grow out of it. They scored food at 1/10.

Ellie aged 6. Two months previously Ellie had choked on a chip, and ever since she was frightened of eating solid food. She chewed a little food using her front teeth until it resembled water. Her mother was worried that this behaviour had become entrenched, and Ellie had lost a lot of weight.

Nutrition

John (9) had been taking iron supplements for a year, and this was changed to a liquid multivitamin and mineral supplement, as the iron could contribute to his feeling sick. We gave Omega oils for bedtime.

After discussion it was agreed that homework was to get 30 stars for trying the following foods: cheese on toast; cottage pie with onion, carrot and gravy; cereal with milk for both breakfast and supper; brown rice, cod, kiwi, banana and baked apples.

At the next session everyone was pleased with progress, and he had gained his 30 stars. His parents were asked to keep a food diary and continue with the star chart, and look up the Slow Food Company on the internet. He was asked to try more protein, and mashed and roast potatoes.

At the third session John was beaming, he had been trying different foods without worrying any more. We recommended continuing with the star chart – two stars for each protein.

Charlie (10) was asked to choose some foods he wanted to try – he chose chicken, cheese, potatoes and peas. It was explained how foods need to be tried fifteen times before being used to eating them, and ways were worked out how he could try these foods by combining them with foods he already ate, to make the transition less stressful. For example, try potato in scrambled egg, and small pieces of chicken in his cream cheese. It was also suggested that Charlie went with his mother to buy the foods in order to take ownership of them, which he was keen to do. A food challenge chart was given. At the next session Charlie had tried a range of new foods, so a list of more new foods was added. By the third session it was reported that Charlie did not get anxious around new foods, and both Charlie and his parents were keen to continue to expand his food groups.

Ellie (6). We discussed what foods Ellie liked and worked out a way to get her back to 'normal' food. She used to like rice crispies for breakfast but found them too scratchy, so it was suggested that she left them soaking in milk to soften them. Better still, have some slippery poached eggs. She liked yoghurt, and we suggested she eat plain bio-yoghurt and add nut butters, coconut cream and fruit. We explained to Ellie that the reason she choked was because she did not chew her food enough and to make sure she ate more slowly to ensure it did not happen again. Epsom salts baths were recommended.

At the second session Ellie had tried scrambled egg with bread for breakfast, and encouragement was given to try toast without crusts, and then with crusts. She had been to a restaurant and had fish and chips. We advised she continue with the star chart and lots of positive encouragement was given. Further encouragement was given at the third session, although they had been on holiday and reported everything was now back to normal.

Massage

John (9) had already had some massages from his mother. Both parents attended and were helpful and interested. A foot massage was started and both mother and father had a turn. They were advised to keep up regular massages at home, which they did, including his younger sister. John was asked to score his Mum on massages and he gave her 9/10. He then had a shoulder and back massage, repeated at the third session.

Charlie (10) was looking forward to having massage, and relaxed well while a foot massage was shown to Mum. They had some massage oil and a handout to continue at home. Next time body massage was demonstrated, and a flower remedy completed.

Ellie (6) enjoyed having some massage and the family went away with oils, handouts, booklet, and a relaxing CD to watch at home. A flower remedy was prepared and supplied.

Being on holiday took them out of their routine but we suggested they at least do some foot massages. A metamorphic technique – light stroking and tapping on the head, hands and feet – was shown and a handout given.

Imagery

John (9). Two magic tricks helped lighten the mood and gain rapport. We told John lots of stories about new foods to help him include them with his favourite foods. At the second session we introduced the Babushka dolls, one of which has an upset face and a story that upsets can be overcome.

A 'rewind' (clearing the emotional element of a memory) was done on this, and we asked John to imagine himself eating cottage pie.

At the third session John was taught a magic trick to entertain his parents, and then some imagery seeing himself in the future succeeding, and imagining what it felt like.

Charlie (10) did his 'special place' which was a rugby field, and a time line was completed from birth until age 10, reframing how much attention he received from his mother. We showed him the emotional freedom technique (EFT) – tapping on set acupressure points – while repeating the words, 'Even though I feel anxious and nervous when I see some chicken on my plate, I am not sure what it will taste like. I am scared I might gag.' He also visualised himself eating and enjoying chicken.

At the second session he went to his special place, again visualising himself enjoying foods that we had specially recommended, i.e. runner beans, barbecued burger, bacon, pizza, pasta, rice, etc. He was asked to continue his EFT at home. At the third session, we explored doing a 'reframe' together on when he was actually sick at the age of 9.

Ellie (6). Rapport was quickly established with lots of laughter, especially from the magic trick taking £1 from her ear. The therapist told two stories about his first and only bout of seasickness, which required him to eat dry toast to feel OK. The second story was about the toy monkey, Monk, who had been chewed by a fox, but who did not like the taste, so he exercised his right of choice by rejecting it. Lots of tricks and laughter again with some suitable positive messages.

The Results

John (9). By the third session both John and his parents were delighted, and said the results were much better than they ever imagined. They brought chocolates and plants as gifts. In a later evaluation they said they most liked the 'relaxed approach and friendly atmosphere which was non-clinical.' They wanted to see a Clover Houses in every county.' The score for food improved from 3/10 to 8/10.

Charlie (10). Charlie's family had spaced out the three appointments in March, April and September. They scored food phobia improved from 1/10 to 8.1/10 and sleep-overs from 2/10 to 10/10 as he had been able to go and stay overnight with friends.

Ellie (5). Ellie's food phobia had disappeared by the second session and she started eating more normally. On the third session she brought a present of a boat fridge magnet in response to the story about the therapist being seasick. Mum wrote a text to say it had been a great experience and close to being a miracle. They scored sleep improved from 3 to 6/10, anxiety improved from 6 to 9/10 and food phobia from 2 to 10/10.

Parent's Letter after treatment for Food Phobia
Dear Clover House,

After Ellie choked on a chip when we were away, we spent the next two months trying to get her back to eating properly. A friend of mine then told me about Clover House. I was at my wits end and thought it sounded like a good idea as Ellie had now lost around half a stone! Which is not what you want for a six year old.

She had also been saying she didn't know if she would get better and she worried about choking all the time, which really saddened me.

When we visited Clover House we saw the imagery therapist first. He wanted to put her at ease which he did very quickly. He asked if she knew why she was there, she said because of her eating and that she'd choked. He told her a couple of stories and a magic trick. After our session, he said that we wouldn't understand what he'd done but that Ellie would take it in.

Then we did massage which Ellie loved. We also had to say out of 10 what we'd score her for eating, 10 being good and 0 being not so good. We put her at a 2.

We then saw Philippa who talked about nutrition and told Ellie that actually her choking was her body looking after her. After we left Ellie was full of her visit. Even though I was desperate for her to get better I didn't want to think this was going to work. So over the next week we put a few new things into practice. And slowly things began to get better.

By the time we went a week later, things were considerably better. When asked what we'd mark her out of 10, I said about a 6 or a 7. They then decided to see Ellie after our holiday to Spain. On returning from holiday her eating was definitely back on track, and she was starting to put on weight. So when they asked what we would mark her out of 10 now, it had to be 10. Ellie was well chuffed and so were we.

Overall, Clover House was a great experience; close to saying it was a miracle.

A Poem by Larry (aged 10)

Clover House is
The place to go
If you're feeling ill
Or low

Bas, Jill and Carole are the
Clover House Team.
When the visit is over
You smile and gleam

Bas helps you to help yourself
Using pictures in your mind.
His jokes are awful, really bad but
He's my friend – and he's kind

Jill does massage
And never hurries.
She soothes away
Your pain and worries

Then there's Carole
Who advises on diet.
Some foods seem strange
But they're nice, just try it!

Clover House is full of fun
You'll be coming back for more.
It's always full of love and care
You're promised that for sure.

Chapter 22

Glue Ear and Hearing Problems

All of the children who came to Clover House with hearing problems due to glue ear conditions were successfully helped. The average score was 2/10 at commencement and 10/10 within 3 sessions. Symptoms of behaviour/frustration averaged 2/10 improved to 7.7/10.

Fiona aged 2 had hearing and communication difficulties. Mum wrote that she was slower than her peers, and could not put two words together. Fiona's frustration manifested itself in hitting, slapping and head banging. She had been diagnosed with glue ear and had had grommets inserted, but these had slipped. They were on the waiting list for speech therapy.

John aged 5 had an ear infection at 18 months and was diagnosed with glue ear at age 2. His mother stated that his behaviour was unpredictable, and that he had been hitting children at school without provocation, and been doing random acts of destruction – knocking things over and upsetting things.

Simon aged 5 came for his behaviour – he would hit, bite, scream, throw toys and furniture. He would not sleep on his own. His mother was exhausted and at her wits' end.

Simon's history revealed that as a baby he had cried constantly day and night, and his parents had repeatedly taken him to the doctor and a children's hospital, where she was told, 'All children cry – it's normal.' The doctor said not to worry, he would not hurt himself, and to put him in babygrows to stop him standing up and biting the cot.

At 18 months old he was eventually discovered to have had ear infections from birth, evidenced by the scarring in his ears. The specialist remarked, 'No wonder he was crying. He must have been in constant pain.'

Nutrition

Fiona (2). It was suggested that Fiona might benefit from removing or reducing dairy foods from her diet as dairy foods are very mucus-forming. We also advised encouraging Fiona to drink very dilute apple cider vinegar to help thin the 'glue' in her ears, and to dilute apple juice with water to reduce sugar content. Another suggestion was to help tone the muscles by drinking thick liquids through a straw. An elderberry tonic was prescribed to help the immune system.

At the second session recommendations were to avoid all wheat products for a few weeks (not too much of a problem as Mum was intolerant of wheat herself) and to have oily fish three times a week to increase essential oil intake. Also to try eucalyptus essential oils in the bath to help clear the tubes and try Hopi ear candles. Acidophilus was given. At the third session it was reported Fiona's stomach was no longer bloated, and that she loved drinking water, eating blueberries and fish. We suggested she continue avoiding diary. Her mother noticed when she had some chocolate her symptoms reappeared.

John (5). We suggested using three 'Cidricial' drops twice a day in juice, and a few drops on cotton wool placed in the ears; natural aloe vera nasal drops as he was having nose bleeds, and also as it might be pollen affecting him. Homework was to eat more fish, restrict dairy and no orange juice. John said his ear and neck was better. He was given supplements of eskimo oil and children's vitamins.

Several factors indicated a lowered immune system, probably due to lots of antibiotics and joint pain in the past, so children's vitamins were prescribed and camomile tea bags for sore eyes. Gradual changes were suggested to come off dairy and food colourings, and to increase healthier foods and snacks.

It was reported Simon was eating fruit instead of biscuits. Acidophilus (good bacteria) supplement was prescribed to help flora balance.

Massage

Fiona (2). As her mother had already attended Clover House with her other child, she already had experience of using massage and some reflexology. At one session when Fiona could not keep still Mum was given Hopi ear candles to use at home.

John (5). Although subdued at first, John came round. He brought his toy duck and Mickey Mouse toys with him. Fun was made of massage, shaking legs and feet until he calmed down. Reflexology points on the big toe were pointed out to Mum to help ear pain, and she should be able to tell if it was working. It was hoped that massage would help John feel more 'noticed' if his behaviour was attention seeking.

At the second session Mum said he had a massage every night for two weeks apart from just two evenings. He enjoyed them. Mum was shown back massage and asked to carry on at home. A flower remedy was made – a magic potion for him to take home.

Simon (5) responded well to massage while his mother and father watched. Explanation was given of energy exchange and being in a caring, positive, relaxed frame of mind. Lavender essential oil was given to use in the bath or vaporiser. Simon later asked Mum to do his massage – apparently she had not done some as a punishment when he was 'bad' for four days. Some parenting handouts were given. Next time his father was able to massage Simon's hands and feet as requested. We reviewed what the aims were, which indicated sleeping was a problem (getting to bed and having nightmares).

Although at the next session Simon was in a 'strop' with his arms folded, he soon changed and again chose his father to do his hands and feet. He said he did not like school, or his teacher. His mother was reminded to change her speech to positive. Dad massaged Simon again and while he had his head massaged, he drifted off to sleep. Dad was amazed and said it was the first time he'd seen him relax in four years.

Imagery

Fiona (2). Mum was very happy and relieved to work on her interactions to relax and help deal with a strong-willed child. As it was found some of Mum's own childhood issues were affecting her relationship with her children, she had some individual sessions to clear some traumas.

John (5). We showed John a magic trick and the Babushka dolls. We noticed that John held his ear with his right hand and stroked his neck on his right side when attention was not on him. When asked about his neck he said it hurt. As the therapist knew body trigger points, he pressed some which seemed to help.

At the second session a new symptom of tummy aches was reported. Work was done with Mum 'rewinding' birth experience (to clear the emotional element of a memory). An incident where John was pinned down at school was reported by Mum, and he was helped to act it out with toys and had a physical 'rewind' session twice, while he laughed.

At the third session, work was done on 'collapsing anchors', interchanging an image of excitement with an image of calm.

Simon (5) responded well to building rapport and changed from reserved to spontaneous. He drew a picture, which was predominately black and red, with some green, of figures and a rainbow. Mum was given a book 'How to talk so kids will listen'.

It was reported that Simon had told his grandfather that his mother did not love him. Simon quickly went to an imagery fantasy in which he gave his temper full rein. The intensity surprised everyone (especially being so young and only the second session).

At the next session he brought his 'cheeky monkey' toy. We worked on his perception that his mother did not love him, his fear-filled dreams and his reaction to the death of his dog. His parents were asked to focus on the positives and change, and further sessions turned out to be great fun.

The Results

Fiona (2). By the second session six weeks later, it was reported her hearing had improved (from 30:40 to 70:40, confirmed by a hospital appointment) and she was talking and singing. At the third session two months later, the hospital hearing test confirmed her hearing near perfect (with just some liquid in the eustachian tubes). Mum reported she was now talking a lot, could contact the outside world and was a confident, happy and friendly little girl. Mum wrote a heartfelt letter of thanks.

John (5). By the second session John said his ear and neck were much better. By the third session Mum had forgotten what they came for as his ear problems had completely disappeared and he was a lot less demanding. They scored behaviour 3 improved to 8/10 and ears from 2 improved to 10/10. Mum rang to cancel a fourth appointment after the school holiday because they did not need it. She said he had made steady progress throughout the holidays and went pottering off in the rock pools, something he would not have done before. She said thank you, she now had her little boy back.

Simon (5). Mum wrote a two-page letter saying how they and others had noticed Simon's change back to being more normal. He no longer had a scowl on his face, he listened and seemed happier, and the violence had disappeared. They scored behaviour from 1 improved to 7.5/10.

Parent's Letter after treatment for Glue Ear

Dear Clover House,

My daughter started displaying behavioural and

emotional changes from about 18 months old. The nursery echoed our concerns that she was unable to hear properly, engage and understand certain things going on around her.

As I was aware of Clover House already due to the fact that they had helped my eldest daughter when she suffered badly with constipation, leading to psychological problems, we knew that was the place to take our youngest daughter.

The team was able to help me deal with all the behavioural and emotional aspects that Fiona experienced. All three of the therapists have such a wonderful and natural way with children and quickly gained the trust of my daughter. The family is treated as a whole and both parent and child feed off of each other; both parties need treating in order to change the dynamics and turn the negative into a positive. Changing my behaviour enabled me to relax and allow my daughter to communi-cate and express in her own way things that may be bothering her, and this helped diffuse our frustration.

Clover House has a wealth of experience healing children and adults alike. There is nothing to fear or be embarrassed about. Clover House is a sanctuary and the children feel comfortable in this homely environment. No one is judged and only patience, care and advice is given.

During our time with Clover House my daughter's behaviour patterns were documented along with various treatments and dietary changes, and this helped us to understand what needed to be put in place in order to help my daughter communicate better and any triggers that made her behave poorly.

It became apparent that my daughter had an allergy which was causing a lot of the problems, primarily the glue ear and runny nose. We have since eliminated dairy and the difference has been significant in quite a short space of time. This was boosted with various vitamins and supplements to build up the immune system.

The NLP brings everything together and as a family it enables you to 'step outside' for a breather and observe objectively your situation and change certain behaviors and habits that can have a detrimental effect on the healing process. A lot of it is done subconsciously after treatment and you find you are able to deal with what life throws at you a lot easier!

As a family we knew we could confide in Clover House due to their professionalism and inviting personalities. They are kind, loving, lots of fun (which the children love about them), and understanding, and they have a desire to help you during your journey with your child.

I believe our daughter is a happier little girl due to the help of Clover House and we are a stronger and healthier family unit. I hope Clover House goes from strength to strength and people become more aware of its services and how it can offer help and advice during times of stress and difficulty and that GPs become aware of the benefits of Clover House.

My thanks and gratitude to you all.

Chapter 23

Headaches and Migraines

All the children we saw at Clover House suffering from headaches and migraines had various other symptoms too, including anger and anxiety. The average scores for all the symptoms were 3.75/10 at commencement and improved to 7.6/10.

The Problems

Jack aged 11 came with a list of complaints including anger, swearing, anxious with obsessive compulsive tendencies, aches, pains and migraines. Mum reported this had all started at age 5, and that he had been permanently excluded from primary school. He had experienced the death of his grandmother.

Mum also reported that she thought Jack had got stuck at age 5 or 6 instead of being age 11. They had had play therapy, been to the child mental health team and had occupational therapy.

Elizabeth aged 11 had dizziness, chest pains, light headedness, headaches, stomach aches, feeling sick, hair loss, shortness of breath during activities, and occasional bedwetting. They had been recommended to Clover House by their doctor.

Stuart aged 9 had headaches and eye problems. The headaches happened when he played on his computer. Mum further explained that he was complaining about tummy aches for the past two weeks. He had disturbed sleep and wanted to get in bed with his parents. She also reported Stuart had loss of appetite and difficulty going to school, and he would not say what was troubling him.

Nutrition

Jack (11). As Jack had said he was interested in rugby and football, he was informed about being healthy to play such sports. Homework was to keep a food diary, and have some supper. Suggestions included having a banana mid-morning, but no oranges, apple or orange juice, and to complete a star chart for eating more vegetables.

Magnesium and Omega fish oil supplements were prescribed. At the next session we advised Jack to have roast beef for iron, and to keep a star chart to encourage eating more fish. Next time he was asked to try salmon and tuna with baked potatoes.

Elizabeth (11). We found Elizabeth had a highly restricted diet and was very reluctant to eat a greater variety of foods. Trying to persuade her took up most of the first consultation. Advice included reducing sweets and chocolate because of high sugar content, to have a protein-rich breakfast to stabilise blood sugar levels, give her more energy and feel less stressed, and to have a small sandwich after school.

Elizabeth continued to reject any suggestions of healthy foods. At the next session she was still eating chocolate before sports and after school, and we explained why vitamins and minerals were needed, and why it was important to keep blood sugar levels balanced. It was suggested that Mum might remove all snacks and chocolate from the house.

We tried to encourage Mum to do more cooking, and Elizabeth to drink more water. Children's multivitamins, minerals and Junior B complex were prescribed. Epsom salts baths and valerian herbal drops were suggested to use at night to aid relaxation.

Stuart (9). We had a general chat with Stuart and introduced the idea of making changes in his eating and drinking. He was asked to start by completing a food diary during the coming week, and to include a list of his moods connected with what he ate. Children's vitamins were given, and healthier foods and drinking water was explained. After having a cola drink later he felt 'funny'. He was also asked to take more exercise. A health project at school coincided, confirming all our advice.

Massage

Jack (11) had a foot massage, during which he visibly relaxed. He already had long wind-downs at bedtime, and Mum was asked to include foot massage. Reflexology points were explained to help with his backache. Mum reported at the next session that Jack had enjoyed foot massages which had been incorporated into their bedtime routine. He had back, shoulder and leg massages. At the third session, because he talked about football he had sports leg massage and pulling of legs and toes and shaking and rocking. Apparently Mum asked Dad to do her feet when in pain and stated, 'It works'.

Elizabeth (11). Mum had done a course on massage through her job, so we demonstrated a massage routine suitable for Elizabeth. We gave her a flower remedy sheet, together with handouts on anxiety and bedwetting.

At the second session the flower remedy was completed (agrimony for hiding problems, aspen for unexplained fears, impatiens for impatience, larch for lack of self confidence, vervain for argumentative and fixed ideas, and vine for strong willed and inflexible). Metamorphic technique (light tapping and stroking of head, hands and feet) was shown at the second session. A full massage was completed at the third session but Mum could only do head massages at home as she had a bad back and neck.

Stuart (9). It was found that Stuart had tense neck and shoulders which were contributing to his headaches. Mum was asked to massage these at home. He enjoyed massage and a full routine was shown next session, although Mum did not have time for massage at home.

Imagery

Jack (11). Mum complained that the main problem was Jack getting into trouble at school, especially if he felt something was unfair. She was unsure whether or not his aches and pains, especially in the mornings, were to do with not wanting to go to school. After discussion Jack said he reacted to being dared by other boys – so new ways of responding were suggested, such as saying, 'Show me how it's done' and 'I missed that, can you show me again', at which he laughed.

A 'blow out' (clearing a habit) was done on when he felt frustrated. Because Jack had problems doing what he was told, we told him some stories about being in the Army and obeying, saluting and not getting caught when doing your own thing.

During a massage, we talked about how to put up with things you don't like, and that sometimes orders are right. This was discussed again at the third session.

Crayons were used to re-create the latest incident at school, and he imagined being the teacher as well as himself.

Elizabeth (11). Most of Elizabeth's symptoms had started when she had an accident at school, when a boy was pushed into her and she fell back on her head. In the sick bay she was very distressed, dizzy and sick. Mum was called and, on taking her to hospital, she became unconscious. Mum was also traumatised from the incident.

A 'rewind' was done to erase the emotion from the memory. This was repeated twice for Mum who kept recalling the emotion associated with the memory.

A garden and sleep flower imagery was given. Elizabeth drew her special garden, and was spending more time drawing, which she enjoyed. She said the hurt in her chest was purple and was asked to change it to yellow, as this colour made her happy.

She often became angry and upset after school and took it out on her Mum, so we showed her the Stein's clenched fist technique, and gave her the idea of drawing a face (of the person who upset her) and scribbling over it to release emotions.

Stuart (9) quickly developed his 'special place' to use every night. As he would not or could not be drawn to any degree, he was told a story about a furry animal who did not know what he knew until he heard himself say it to somebody else. Stuart then said his tummy was 'normal' after school, especially on Fridays! At the next session he wanted to work on his fear of dogs which was helped by contact during sessions with a local dog.

The Results

Jack (10). By the second session Jack reported feeling different – with more energy and concentration. His behaviour had also improved so much that school had forgotten to do his regular Friday meetings. He had been commended at assembly. At the third session he scored improvements in migraines from 3 to 9/10, pains from 4 to 8/10 and reacting better 4 to 7/10. At an evaluation one month later Mum wrote that, 'It has provided Jack with a much better diet, which has benefited the whole family.' She scored 8/10 improvement on her child's symptoms.

Elizabeth (11). Within three sessions Elizabeth scored sleep from 4/10 improved to 8/10, anxiety 4/10 to 8/10 . No further mention was made of the list of symptoms including headaches.

Stuart (9). Throughout his sessions Stuart became happier and more confident. He won a merit for his piano playing. He reported feeling happier and having more energy. At his final session he reported walking past a large dog on his own. He also said he felt 10/10. He scored worry improved from 2/10 to 9/10.

Chapter 24

Hyperactivity

Averge scores on hyperactivity at commencement were 4.5/10 improving to 8.5/10. Other symptoms experienced by children with hyperactivity began at 3.6/10 and improved to 8/10. The average number of sessions was three.

The Problems

Molly aged 11 had been hypersensitive, hyperactive, aggressive, with difficulty in focusing, and a lack of empathy since she was 2–3 years old. Her mother thought it was partly hereditary and partly started by the MMR jab. She also recorded that she had had a long and difficult labour, and that it had taken her three months to really bond with Molly.

They had been through the school for help, the school nurse and the paediatric department at hospital. Her mother had written a letter to the doctors explaining how she thought Molly's behaviour was like a toddler – even when asked to sit still and not touch things, for example at the optician's – she was up, touching, asking what is this, what is that, etc. At school she was made to sit at the front to avoid distractions. She played rough and her mother could see she was not being invited to parties.

Mum reported that since Molly reached puberty, both her and her partner had been scratched, kicked, punched and sworn at. They were desperately asking for help, and worried about Molly attending secondary school.

Steve aged 12. Steve's parents were recommended to contact us by a National Hyperactive Support Group. Steve had been removed from his birth family at age 3, fostered for two years, before being adopted at age 5. Six years ago he had been diagnosed by a family clinic as being oppositional. His parents understood about additives, sweeteners and preservatives increasing his bad behaviour. His mother wrote that he had a craving/emptiness which he felt money or things would satisfy, and this had led to stealing and lying. Steve had said he missed his previous family and that was why he behaved as he did.

Luke aged 9 had also been recommended by the Hyperactive Support Group, who had recorded Luke as hyperactive, swearing, wanting constant attention, verbally and physically aggressive, not sleeping, and sleeping with his mother. This had been apparent since he was 18 months old. He was soiling and not getting to sleep until 1 am. Luke attended a special needs school. They had tried the child mental health service, social services, and had done a parenting programme.

Nutrition

Molly (11) was observed as being fidgety and a little overweight. She liked vegetables but tended to eat a lot of chocolate, crisps and sugary tea. So we advised her to cut down on these and replace puddings and snacks by having more home-cooked meals with lots more vegetables, and also to cut down on noodles and pasta.

We also suggested she replace the sugary tea with diluted fruit juice. The family was advised about blood sugar balance and also how her hormones may partially account for moodiness and weight gain. Molly was prescribed magnesium morning and night time, and Omega oils, Epsom salts for bathing, and had a blood sugar balance handout.

By the second session she had made amazing progress, having eaten no sweets or sugar, having crackers and cheese instead, and only one pudding at school during the week, with just one treat of a packet of crisps and one cup of tea. It was suggested she change the treat to one or two squares of 70% dark chocolate, and to try new foods such as hummus and nut butters.

At the third session her mother had found virtually sugar-free chocolate and sugar-free jelly. Breakfast was suggested to be bacon and eggs (not crackers), and to sit down at the table and eat breakfast before watching any TV.

Steve (12) was found to be aware of what happened when he ate the wrong foods, but since starting secondary school, his parents had less control over his eating. As he seemed full of mucus, reducing dairy foods was suggested. Also to change supplements to professional makes known to the nutritionist.

At the second session Steve's mother was recommended to get rid of all 'bad foods' from the house and replace them with healthy choices to prevent temptation and show solidarity. If, as suspected, he had a dairy intolerance, then he should completely avoid all dairy products for at least two weeks, and then monitor symptoms. Blood sugar balance was explained and how eating refined foods could affect mood throughout the day, and we suggested that the blood sugar diet was tried.

A practical demonstration of cross crawling was explained for every morning, which might help his concentration. An ADHD handout, blood sugar balance and lunchbox ideas handouts were given, with suggestions of Omega oils and bio-acidophilus supplements. At the second session Steve was disinterested. His father attended and reported that he had had sweets in school and had then got into trouble.

Steve's irritability had improved. Motivation was given on gradually introducing new foods with our food challenge chart. We found he was having a sugar cereal for breakfast so we asked him to change this to muesli with yoghurt, nuts and seeds, and chopped fruit. Further recommendations were to increase oily fish with salmon or mackerel in sandwiches, and to increase the protein content of meals (equivalent to carbohydrate). We also suggested he have some homemade apple cake or flapjacks with extra oats to replace sweet foods. Magnesium supplements were prescribed to help fidgeting.

At the third session it was found Steve was spending his paper-round money on sweets and energy drinks, which made him aggressive. We encouraged him to control his eating especially at home in order to compensate snacking with friends and at school.

Luke (9). Luke's mother had started doing some dietary work after reading the Clover House booklet, and reduced his crisp intake (from four a day to one a week) and encouraged him to eat more vegetables. From the National Organisation Support Group he was already taking Omega 3 supplements, zinc and magnesium.

We explained to Luke how eating carbohydrates was contributing to his aggression, and that eating a protein-rich breakfast would help. Ideas were given for healthier snacks, and to drink more water, and to dilute any fruit juice. We recommended him to do after school activities to act as a stress buster, and try Epsom salts baths for relaxing. We gave him our food challenge chart to encourage him to try new foods fifteen times. The blood sugar handout was given, and advice to increase the magnesium and Omega 3 intake.

At the second session Luke had been trying new vegetables, and his mother had been putting lots of vegetables into casseroles, rewarding him with a small toy at the end of the week. He was being encouraged to play with his friends at the playground and go to holiday club. They were asked to keep to regular meals and snacks as his temper could be due to hunger, and for Luke himself to get something to eat when he began to feel irritable.

At the third session although he said he did not like vegetables, his mother was still disguising them in stews, and he reported liking bread rolls filled with salad. His mother was giving him food when he was getting argumentative and not talking to him. He reported starting some new activities, i.e. swimming, adventurers and karate.

Massage
Molly (11). A massage routine was shown to Molly's mother and father and discussion was held to obtain scores. A flower remedy handout was given for completion. At the second session they had all done very well and had been doing a massage every night. The flower remedy was completed. At the third session the metamorphic technique was shown.

Steve (12). We found that Steve was not always polite and crossed the boundaries to being rude. His parents complained of his lack of respect, yet they let his behaviour go during the session. It was suggested he gets into trouble because he is bored at school. He then got in with the trouble makers and they were leading each other on into more trouble.

Steve's parents were shown massage, which they were willing to try at home. By the next session massage had been going well and Steve had been sleeping better. More massage was done. Again it was noticed that his parents did not correct his behaviour, so the therapist did.

At the next session Steve had complained about the massages at home. We demonstrated techniques again in order to identify the problem, and it seemed his father had not done massage firmly enough for him. We reinforced the message that being rude or stroppy was not acceptable. At their fourth session, Steve had been doing a lot of sports and appreciated leg massage. His mother learned more too.

Luke (9) was falling asleep within 10 minutes of having his feet and hands massaged. Mum was asked to do massage at home. He came to sessions with his brother, so there was a bit of rivalry for attention, both had some massage. Motivation was given for his mother to keep doing the massages at home. Luke also made up his own flower remedy.

Imagery

Molly (11) opened up and said it was the first time she had answered questions about her anger, and verbally admitted it to anyone. As this was the first time she had talked about it, she was congratulated and told that we have to acknowledge a problem before we can work on it.

Her anger was only expressed at home. She did recall an incident when she was 4 years old of her father being violent towards her mother and a 'rewind' (a technique to reduce the emotional element of a memory) was completed on this. After some discussion, Molly realized that she suppressed her anger, which then came out unexpectedly, especially when she could not have what she wanted.

Ways to deal with anger without being violent were suggested, including Stein's clenched fist technique (clenching the anger in the fist and then releasing it), breathing and blowing out the anger, thumping on the bed with thumbs folded under fingers, and drawing a face of the person she was angry with and scribbling over it. Her parents were asked to look for triggers for her anger. They asked for the last session to be used to address Molly's lack of patience.

We learned that after having had one miscarriage and wanting a baby so much, her mother immediately responded to Molly's every wish. So a discussion was had about instant gratification, and learning as an adult that waiting or saving can be equally or possibly more gratifying. We did a visualisation with Molly, meeting herself as a baby, and continuing up to the present day, being loved, being taught to be patient, and not being responded to immediately. An 'anchor' was set (first finger and thumbs touching), and taking three deep breaths whenever anyone said No to her.

By the second session Molly expressed that it had worked, as she had not lost her temper all week, and she had been rewarded by getting two pet rats. The family had completed an agreement/contract between them all about rules on looking after them and all the behaviour and commitments for Molly including the nutrition, massage and imagery homework.

We then discussed learned behaviour and modelling good behaviour, which was taken on board by the parents. At this session Molly was able to say that her anger started in her throat and made her scream. Regarding anger at school, she decided to use the blowing out anger technique. Advice was given about respect, and that losing her temper at home was not respectful to her parents. We also had a discussion about mutual respect.

Steve (12). It was noted Steve's parents spoke for him. Rapport was made by the therapist pretending to have difficulty reading, which led to Steve laughing but then we asked if he understood how that would make the other person feel, and referred this back to school. After talking and hearing Steve's story, he was persuaded to access his 'emptiness', and a 'blow out' was completed which left Steve surprised and laughing.

At session two, being more relaxed, using crayons Steve did a play theatre of his natural parents, foster family, and adopted parents all between 2 and 6 year old. A 'rewind' was done on this, with suggestions of how well he was doing. His mother asked for work to be done on his attitude to school, so future disassociation was done.

However at the next session he was not easy to engage, but after 30 minutes we worked on 'fair' and 'not fair'. His parents asked for some help in parenting and language, being positive, and motivating. They were advised to change words such as 'should' and 'must' and instead use 'want to' and 'going to', and to set up a specific place in the house for reprimanding him and setting boundaries.

Steve needed to work on his self esteem without his parents, and he was asked to use an idea of 'seeing himself' and asking this visible self to tell him in a few weeks how he was. He was able to express that his visible self was sad a lot of the time, but also happy sometimes. So we worked on a technique for that and then asked Steve to contact his visible self again; the message was that he was happy and knew about it. Asked about being sad, Steve said he checked it was now OK.

Luke (9) started with his special place, which was a secure garden and playground with climbing equipment and a trampoline which he used until exhausted. We showed him a toy dog who had his own trampoline, water and food bowls, and tree. The dog held his anger in his chest area and we taught Steve Stein's clenched fist to let go of anger. His mother reported having gone onto the website for special needs children to use a 'turtle' technique (being in a shell, calm and peaceful) and we practised this too.

The special place was re-enforced the next time, and other toys joined him. Luke reported that there was a small child of about 18 months crying, and Luke asked him what was wrong. He was told he was missing his mummy. Luke reassured him and told him he was safe and not alone and played with him.

At the third session Luke learned that his mother did not listen to him when he was angry, and he now had chill out time, and recognised his own need for space when angry. He went off for 10 minutes when he used the special place or turtle technique. The session included talking, listening and congratulating, and re-enforcing the techniques.

Results

Molly (11). At her third and final session, cards and presents were given out. Both parents and Molly were pleased and declared it had worked. Their scores were: Aggression from 1/10 to 9/10, hyperactive from 6/10 to 9/10 and hypersensitive from 5/10 to 9/10.

In an email two months later Molly's mother confirmed scores for aggression and hyperactive to 10/10 and that the whole family had noticed an amazing transformation. They were all a lot less stressed. She also wrote that Molly was managing her diet, and taking her supplements and that she had enjoyed her visits. Mum and her partner 'had learned a lot, she could see how it started, but they were both now putting in the effort to all three daughters, and that it was a two way thing.'

Steve (12). Throughout the sessions Steve made improvements in food, mood, and behaviour. They scored school work improved from 5 to 6/10, being respectful from 4 to 6/10 and fighting with brother from 5 to 10/10.

Luke (9). After the first session Luke's behaviour started to improve and he had been sleeping from 10 pm instead of 1 am, with steady improvement in his hyperactivity. His scores improved significantly and after two months Mum completed our evaluation form as follows:

Calm 2.5 to 6.5 to 8/10
School 3.5 to 5.5 to 8/10
Soiling 3.5 to 7.5 to 8/10
Brother 5 to 7 to 8.5/10
Fear on own 0 to 4 to 5.5/10
Sleeping on own from 0 to 9/10

Mum scored us 10/10 on changes, and continued use of techniques and success, and she most liked 'not being judged'. She achieved 'normality, calm and reduced stress'.

The Clover House Gang
A Poem by Wayne and his Mum

When I arrive, their dogs Ruby and Rudge
Welcome me with a lick and a nudge.
They are so sweet, I'd like to give them a treat.
When I leave, I say a sad goodbye
But its only a week and time soon goes by.

Baz helps me relax and it makes me feel good.
I promise to do my homework like I should.
Carole helps me with diet and vitamin pills,
So I will get better and not feel so ill.
And there is Jill with her soothing hand,
Whose healing massage makes me feel grand.

I love Clover House,
Its like a safe second home.
If I feel troubled or sick,
I can always phone.

Chapter 25

IBS, Tummy Problems & Crohn's Disease

A ll children who came with IBS (irritable bowel syndrome) and tummy ache symptoms improved significantly. They also came with a wide variety of other symptoms, mainly associated with anxiety. The average score commenced at 3/10 and improved to 8.5/10 in an average of 2.8 sessions.

The Problems

Andy aged 8 had had constipation for years. His mother wrote that he also had anxieties and that these had increased ten fold in the past six months. His teacher said he needed some help. He feared assembly, being sick, and did not want to do sports. He would not go upstairs or sleep upstairs on his own. She wrote that it hadn't helped that he witnessed his father (separated from mother) falling down the stairs and watched him as he lay unconscious. Since then he felt sick at the slightest event.

David aged 13 had 'always' been suffering from anxiety. He had suffered IBS for the past two years, and psoriasis, a skin condition, for the past six months. The doctor had recommended Clover House several years ago, and David had been tested for Crohn's and coeliac disease. They scored anxiety at 2/10; sleep 4/10; skin 0/10; and IBS at 2/10.

Issey aged 12 was suffering from IBS, anxiety and mood swings. She hated being away from her mother, and was jealous of her brother. Her IBS symptoms started with constipation when she was age 4.

Nutrition

Andy (8) was born with an enlarged kidney. His mother had this checked out again, and it was still the same. Andy was twitching in his left eye, had other twitches and was squeezing his hands. In addition to nutritional advice, we asked them to do a food diary and a star chart. A magnesium supplement was prescribed to have at night, and a digestive enzyme at breakfast time and after the evening meal.

At the second session Andy was eager to do his goal scores, and said that he felt sick and embarrassed at his father shouting at everyone in front of his friends. He had not visited his father for six weeks because he was reluctant. He was asked to continue with the star chart for vegetables and salad.

David (13) was recommended to try to avoid all dairy foods to see if they were causing his IBS, especially as he was having dairy foods in excess. We explained the importance of blood sugar levels and that this might be an underlying cause of his psoriasis – he was also having a lot of cola drinks. Examples of foods to have for breakfast and snacks after school were given. We suggested Epsom salts baths to increase magnesium levels and help relaxation. A blood sugar handout was given and a suggestion of Rhodiola, a supplement for stress, for when he was feeling anxious.

By the second session it was reported that David had managed to keep to a dairy free diet. Further advice was to try Swedish glaze soya ice cream and mozzarella cheese; to try having a fruit soya or tofu smoothie before school, and to try fresh mackerel once or twice a week to help his psoriasis. Also to apply vitamin E cream on his skin. By the third session he had been having some salmon as his oily fish, and was going to try pilchards.

Issey (12) enjoyed all kinds of foods and had a big appetite. Trigger foods seemed to be garlic, cheese (which she loved) peas and tomato skins.

It was advised that IBS is often caused by food intolerance, and indeed Issey said that dairy products made her feel worse, so it was suggested that she avoid *all* dairy foods for a week. Dairy-free alternatives were given.

Other recommendations were to have a protein-rich breakfast, to eat all her school dinner, and having a balanced mid-morning snack, which would help balance her blood sugar levels, her mood and help anxiety. We asked her to avoid all cola drinks due to their caffeine content and dilute fruit juice with half water, and to try linseeds for constipation. Supplements of B vitamins, digestaid and acidophilus powder given.

After an update at the second session the tummy aches were still bad, especially on Sunday when stressed about school next day. We suggested she grind the linseeds before soaking, and avoid eggs for the next week, replacing them with bacon or ham. To try Rhodiola for stress and Epsom salts baths. We also suggested having a hot water bottle on her stomach to help the pain.

Other suggestions included keeping a food diary to see if

there was any relationship between food eaten, eating times and bloating. Also to have digestive enzymes at lunch time, and a colon cleanse, and try cider apple vinegar.

At the fourth session we asked her to avoid all the foods to which she had an intolerance for at least two months, and to talk to the GP about further investigations. Her mother had a theory that this may be related to the attention her brother was getting because of his ill health.

Massage

Andy (8). Andy's first session began with foot massage, and although he was quiet and shy at first, he became more relaxed. Mum was hesitant at first about trying the massage, but became more confident as she practised. They were given massage oils and a handout, and asked to try some foot massages at home. Andy appeared angry at his mother during our sessions, and was critical of her saying 'harder or too gentle'. Back and shoulder massages were shown.

David (13). David's mother was very keen on reflexology as it had helped her sister, so a foot routine was shown. They were given some massage oils, handouts and a relaxing CD. As David was a teenager he did not want massage, so his mother was shown metamorphic technique (a gentle tapping and stroking over the head, hands and feet). His mother was also anxious.

At the third session it was reported that David liked the new technique she had learnt.

Issey (12). Issey's mother was reminded of massage techniques and some reflexology moves and they were given some oils, a handout and a flower remedy sheet to complete. The second session concentrated on the tummy and colon areas of the foot (middle sole area) and advice about deep breathing into the abdomen. Flower remedies were completed.

As the tummy aches still persisted, they reported that Mum had been rubbing Issey's tummy but not her feet as Issey was nervous that it might hurt.

Issey complained about this at the third session, but we suggested that the tenderness would lessen as it was worked, and it did. We asked them to include emotions and situations in the food diary.

Imagery

Andy (8) was able to do a 'rewind' (a technique to clear emotional element of a memory) on the incident that he wanted to deal with (which he decided not to disclose). He was then introduced to the Babushka dolls and the story in which the second to last doll has an upset face and sometimes in life things happen but you can get over it.

A 'dream arm' (with an autosuggestion that when you go to sleep it will make sure you have good dreams) was installed and Andy chose Dr Who as his super-hero, who would come to his aid in any bad dreams.

At the second session, as Andy was concerned about a spot on his elbow, he did 'vanish a condition' imagery to ameliorate the pain.

He said his father's shouting still upset him, so 'collapsing anchors' (where an emotional state is anchored to a sound or movement and is then changed/collapsed with a positive sound and anchor). He chose to use the noise of football as a positive resource.

David (13) came with his mother and father and they all discussed his history. His mother had had a bad time during pregnancy, and as a baby David found it difficult to sleep. His sister was born when he was 2, and she had a heart defect and was in intensive care.

David could remember an incident when his Mum had screamed, thinking his sister was dead, and when his father had a bad accident. He now walks with a stick and is partially blind.

All three of them joined in imagery, starting with slow deep breaths and slow exhalations, to demonstrate to David how he could learn to control his body. David's special place was on the floor with dogs on his lap, a pond, fishes, horses, pets that had died, and wild life around. He felt happy and peaceful. Asked what he felt most scared of he replied 'The unknown', and 'fear of losing everyone around me.' His mother then disclosed that this was her fear also. At the second session David had used his happy place when the teacher had been shouting at school.

We again had a lot of discussion about family incidents and traumas. David had missed a school trip last year because of his IBS, and found that his fear was of other people's bad behaviour and that someone (maybe himself) might be injured. A rewind was done with his parents on the bad pregnancy, bad birth, and an operation. At the end of the rewinds, the pictures in their minds had changed to something pleasant.

David was asked to visit his happy place and to find a path where, as he went along it, he met himself as a baby. A time-line technique was used to tell the baby exactly what the baby needed to hear, and phrases such as, 'You are loved, you are safe, your family is safe, they love and support you,' and to bring all those feelings and that knowledge forward to present day. His mother burst into tears as she had found it very moving.

At the third session David's mother reported that she was being far more assertive, and asking family members to change from being negative to positive. A rewind was done on the events leading up to last year's school trip, and then a progression was made to imagine himself on the morning of the next trip, getting up, feeling fine, seeing himself on the coach and enjoying the trip. Then we repeated it again.

Issey (12). After discussion of her history and present situation, it was mentioned that the family had been involved in a car crash, which was thought to have contributed to her separation anxieties. Her mother and Issey were asked to take a deep breath, close their eyes and imagine they were in their special happy places. Issey's was a beach in the Caribbean – clear seas, warmth, horses and dolphins. Her best friend was there with her mother, father, grandmother and dog (notice no brother!) A rewind was done on the car accident.

At the second session Issey's mother was stressed with the sibling rivalry as both children were sleeping in her bedroom. Issey felt that her mother did not spend enough time with her and although it was suggested she do a chart of the time they do spend together, she was reluctant. Her mother also said that Issey tended to look on the negative side and Issey said she had worrying thoughts going round in her head. They were asked to do their special place and we suggested that Issey find a path where she met herself at the age of 4 – when her constipation began – and was told it was okay to let it come out.

Next we created an image of a 'What If?' bin. Issey's was purple and round with a lid and a letter box for posting 'What Ifs?' and all her negative thoughts.

At the third session Issey was encouraged to speak to her stomach, acknowledge the pain and let it know it had been heard and that she was in the process of changing her diet to food that was acceptable to her stomach. Also she did a pain management technique of imagining using a control switch in her head to turn down the pain.

At the fourth session we discussed parenting issues with her mother. Again Issey was encouraged to speak to her stomach, and practised slow breathing to counteract her tension.

The Results

Andy (8). Within one month and at the second session Andy scored his tummy pains improved from 2 to 9/10; happy at school went from 5 to 7/10, and not to be upset from 4 to 9/10.

David (13). By his second session David's mother reported her anxiety had improved from 3 to 6/10. At the third session David scored his psoriasis from 0 to 6/10, sleep improved from 4 to 8/10, anxiety from 2 to 7/10, and his IBS from 2 to 9/10.

Issey (12). At her fourth session Issey's scores had improved: anxiety from 3 to 9/10, IBS from 2 to 6/10. Her school attendance was returning to normal and foods to which she was intolerant were being eliminated from her diet.

Parent's Letter after treatment for IBS and Crohn's Disease
Dear Clover House,

My son has suffered with severe Crohn's disease since he was a baby. For 14 years life was full of tests, needles, medication, nasal-gastric feeding, catheters, and hospitalisations. There was the threat of a colostomy, and my son was too unwell to attend mainstream school. Every day he was living with pain, diarrhoea, sickness, blood loss, weight loss. Our whole life was upset and for 14 years he needed 24 hour care. Even not sleeping for days on end. I have two other children who are thankfully well, but they have suffered, as my son's need was continuous.

In December my son's illness took a turn for the worse, and he was admitted to hospital to enable morphine to be prescribed for 4 days. I had not slept, my son grabbing an odd 20-minute naps here and there. His stomach was rock hard; he hadn't eaten or drunk for days. The four days drained me of caring, I could not care any longer, I was exhausted. It felt as though I had been by his bedside for the past 14 years, sleeping on a chair while he was hospitalised. When they gave him morphine and he was able to sleep, with no pain, I made a promise then and there that there has to be another answer to Ben's health. I did not want my son to rely on morphine, nasal gastric feeding and medication as a way to live.

My son's illness was destroying his life; he has not experienced friendships, going to school, or a carefree everyday life that other healthy children have. He would watch lads play through the window. He had to be by a toilet at all times, going to the toilet about 11 times a day, and about five times at night. My son had expressed that life was too hard to carry on, that the pain was too much.

I discussed with his Dad that we had to try something else, that for all the 14 years with hospital treatments they have not worked for our son. It took me weeks of searching, when I came across a leaflet for Clover House saying, 'We treat the child, not the illness.'

I found this comforting, as I was careful not to do anything that would harm Ben. So after filling out a sample questionnaire I had an appointment within a few days to go to Clover House.

Now remember I had not ventured in this area before; however, we went with an open mind. We were greeted with open arms, which I found astonishing, as with hospitals there can be long waiting times and no affection. I had built up a wall over the past 14 years, so I was very careful. I spoke for my son a lot of the time, as it was normal with hospitals, the doctors would speak to me over Ben's head, but Clover House wanted to listen to Ben. At first I found this hard, but soon realised he can speak for himself, as they wanted to listen to him, and what he had to say was important.

He spent time with imagery, this enabled Ben to express his thoughts and feelings and fears, and express his concerns unconditionally. He was able to say when he's unhappy with his lifestyle of pain. He imagined away his pain as knives to be melted away.

Ben had sessions with nutrition, and advice on his diet; he is on goat's milk, yeast-free bread, no preservatives, no artificial colourings or flavourings, no fizzy drinks and only plain crisps. He had vitamins and time was spent teaching us both about nutrition and Ben has improved immensely.

With aromatherapy, Ben and I have found this very beneficial, as I feel re-charged. I have plenty of love and care to give. I have been taught to massage Ben – and my other children.

Ben is confident and for the first time in his life he can go out and has made friends. He feels he does not have to be chained to a toilet, or watch through the window at other kids – he is out there with them. His medication which was at high doses is coming down – this is a first.

Ben is well! He looks healthy, the darkness has gone. He is starting to grow again; he had stopped growing for four years. He has suffered no pain or discomfort and wants to live, because he now says, 'Life's worth living.'

My wall has come down, and the change that I wished for has happened. A smile on my son's face, a smile of happiness, no pain, no discomfort, a smile of contentment.

I now have three healthy children. Ben needs to be aware of his diet. He has a lot of years to catch up on and looks forward to a normal life.

If anyone has an ill child, do not give up when everything looks hopeless, seek and find alternatives. As I took that frightening step, it all worked out better than I could have imagined.

Chapter 26

Myalgic Encephalopathy (M.E.) and Chronic Fatigue Syndrome

T he majority of the children who came to Clover House for chronic fatigue, or Myalgic Encephalopathy (ME), or Post Viral Fatigue Syndrome, scored their symptoms substantially improved, and even cleared completely, i.e. scored 10/10). The average number of sessions was 2.75. Associated symptoms included poor sleep, nausea, tiredness, headaches, sore throat, stress, low energy, lack of confidence and anger.

Colin aged 13 had been suffering for two years since the age of 11 when he had tonsillitis and appendicitis with repeated antibiotics. Eventually his paediatrician confirmed chronic fatigue. Now he was only able to attend school for a few sessions a week and used a rest room at the school. He wanted improvement in his symptoms of being tired, nauseated and sleepless, with headaches and sore throat.

John aged 14. Mum wrote that John's chronic fatigue had got worse in the last eight months, 'to the point that he is not able to go to school, feeling sick, has tummy aches, sore throats, no energy and not sleeping well.' She also reported that John was feeling very low and angry, was frustrated at not getting to school and missing out on his friends and often cried.

He was sleeping in his parent's bedroom and got upset when he woke up. She reported negative atmosphere all round in the home, with Dad not liking the sleeping arrangements, Mum nagging John to get up and have a routine (advised by hospital consultant), together with John and his sister's sibling rivalry.

Additionally John was dyslexic, small for his age and had been bullied at school. His flower remedy choices were for having fears and worries, feeling hopeless and pessimistic, unexplained gloom, exhausted in body and mind, at the limits of his endurance, feeling resentful and 'poor me'.

Clare aged 8. The paediatrician had diagnosed Clare who had been suffering since having an injection at age 3. She was always tired and had a low immune system. She had regularly had tonsillitis from 8 months to 2 years old, with prolonged use of antibiotics, and never recovered after having her tonsils out. She had outbursts of anger and wanted to improve her sleep, confidence and her anger.

Nutrition

Colin (13) and his mother had a talk about balancing his blood sugar levels to give him stable energy and allow his adrenal glands to rest. They were advised to change to protein-rich meals and to increase his vegetable intake. Also to change his sugary snacks to higher protein, i.e. hummus and carrots, cheese on oatcakes. To have more liquid meals which are easier to digest, such as smoothies made from bio-yogurt, tofu, nut butters and fruit. Also to have blended soups with significant protein from meat, fish, pulses, etc. for one to two meals a day. To have a snack such as crackers and cheese and dark hot chocolate before bedtime to prevent blood sugar levels dropping and waking him.

Other advice included having an Epsom salts bath at bedtime to help relaxation. A summary sheet and blood sugar balance handouts were given, together with vitamin D, zinc, fish oils and a multivitamin, and an elderberry tonic. Mum was asked to add CoQ10 and D-Ribose 5g three times a day.

The following session included motivation to fully incorporate the above changes. Further suggestions included getting some valerian herbal tincture to put in bedtime milk to help sleep, and to try progressive muscle tensing and relaxing.

John (14). We explained to Mum and John how stress may be effecting his immune system, digestion and sleep patterns. Essential fatty acids found in oily fish and nuts will support his immune system, and help his dyslexia. They were asked to follow an eating plan which kept his blood sugar levels stable throughout the day. We gave him a blood sugar balance handout, and suggested having Epsom salts baths to increase magnesium levels and help relax for sleep, plus a supplement of D-Ribose to help boost energy levels. We reminded them that all new foods need to be tried at least fifteen times.

Because John was not keen on eating many vegetables Mum was given a five-vegetable tomato sauce recipe. A suggestion of ginger tea was given to reduce nausea, and to keep to regular meal times.

Clare (8) was found to have a very restricted diet (of toast, coco pops, pitta bread, crackers, fishcakes, chicken dippers and smiley faces. Mum said she was frightened of trying new foods.

We explained about needing to try any new foods fifteen times before they were accepted. Some meals were suggested, i.e. for breakfast, scrambled egg and toast; for lunch, chicken sandwich, lettuce and salad cream; at tea time, home made chicken goujons. We gave them our food challenge chart handout and recommended supplements of acidophilus pro-biotics and children's multivitamin and minerals.

At the second session Clare had filled in her new challenge chart with five new foods, but would not accept scrambled egg or roast chicken, but she was taking her supplements. Further suggestions included, if she liked sausages, buying good quality ones, and for Mum to keep giving her small amounts of new healthy foods with her usual favourites to help gain acceptance as she needed good nutrition to regain strength and vitality. We asked Mum not to let her regress with her eating. We suggested she think of good things like riding her pony when eating, and imagine her body filling with her favourite colour (gold) when she ate new foods.

By the third session Clare was still reluctant about eating new foods. We suggested that she help her mother make the foods she likes, such as homemade yogurt with flake and fruit, homemade chicken dippers, fish cakes and, as she loved chocolate cake, a homemade version with ground almonds, extra eggs, grated carrot, beetroot and courgette.

Massage

Colin (13). Mum was shown massage and metamorphic technique which she thought would be useful for all her children. Colin loved his massage so the family accepted a massage bed to use at home. A breathing technique handout was given as well as a relaxation tape.

John (14). Mum was shown foot massage (reflexology) and received a flower remedy sheet to complete. John was additionally having cupping technique elsewhere.

Mum and John were still negotiating about him wanting the latest X-box game and Mum saying she would buy it if he did his homework. This led to discussion about parenting and that being ill can have benefits, for example, attention. Or it can be a defence against growing up issues, etc. Mum took this on board, especially as Dad had recently rebuked John for asking his mother to fetch and carry for him.

Clare (8). As they were on a tight time scale, we gave Clare and her mother a quick demonstration of foot massage, and our DVD, together with a flower remedy sheet to complete. More massage techniques were demonstrated next time, as well as metamorphic technique (a light tapping and stroking of the head, hands and feet).

Clare had tense neck and shoulders. Mum was also under stress as she was defending her daughter from the school about time off regarding her illness. The flower remedies included aspen for unexplained fears, impatiens for impatience, mimulus for a fear of spiders, and olive for exhaustion.

Imagery

Colin (13) had a discussion about imagery and about information feeding into his subconscious. He created a special place to use at bedtime. We also discussed family dynamics, especially as he did not get on with his sister. He experimented with controlling his behaviour and observing what effect this had on his sister, and their relationship.

We also suggested that Mum should make some house rules and boundaries, and if they argued, then they should be separated or sent to their own rooms.

At the second session Colin said he had five special places and practised one in the woods, with long grass and buttercups, feeling happy and enjoying the freedom. Mum also did her special place to help her relax.

Colin took on board the discussions and was more aware. He said he knew he would get better and had made up his mind he will be fully in control of his chronic fatigue by the time he starts the new school year in September.

John (14). Both Mum and John were asked to imagine their special place. Mum's was on a beach on holiday, and John's was in his bed! John was asked to imagine a garden and to include 'sleep flowers'. After discussion, it seemed the cause of John's ME might be from when he went away with his father on a rugby trip (Dad being the rugby coach), when John was sick, had a sore throat and uncomfortable stomach.

At the second session John was asked to close his eyes and contact his stomach ache and what was it telling him – 'Something's wrong, and it's really bad – I need help.'

He was asked what help he needed and he replied,

'Someone to help me feel better, advice on what to do, tablets, reassurance, people understanding what I'm going through.'

John was asked to take a deep breath, close his eyes and imagine he was in his special happy place. Then we did a 'rewind' (to remove the emotional element of a memory) on the coach journey when he was sick. John was asked to contact his stomach ache and ask the initial cause – he replied 'Exhaustion'.

He was then asked to imagine a mini-John who went down to his stomach to see what was happening down there. He said he stomach was full of green, caused by a green bug flame. Using his imagination, a dragon rider came to control the fire, and mini-John picked up the bug and put it in his pocket.

We then discussed what could be the causes of his exhaustion, and he commented, 'Lots of people have high standards. I have to be the best for Dad.'

Clare (8). At her first session Clare said her tummy was hungry but her head was telling her not to eat. A handout on EFT (Emotional Freedom Technique of tapping on acupressure points while saying positive phrases) was given, and we did some practise. Her special place was sitting at home with the family watching TV.

Because as a young child she had been unable to swallow and been hospitalised and put on a drip, we gave her further tapping phrases such as, 'Even though I'm scared to try something new I don't like the taste, the texture. Even though I'm scared to try something new I'm scared the food won't go down, I'll choke on it, I'll gag, it'll hurt, I'll be ill again, and I'll have to go back to hospital,' while tapping meridian energy lines to clear negative blocks.

With her reluctance to try new foods or do the tapping, we agreed she would do one phrase at bedtime and each time a new food was introduced, one phrase at a time.

A rewind was done on the tonsillitis, represented by a red square, and a 'progression', a picture in her mind, and affirmation 'I can eat everything, lots of foods I can eat'.

Results

Colin (13). Within three sessions over three months, Colin reported clearance of his tiredness, nausea, sore throat and headaches, scoring them all at 10/10. He scored sleep from 0 to 5/10.

John (14) came on his own for two sessions and one further session with his sister, who had also been having sessions for her own health complaints. He scored improvements in sleep from 1 to 10/10, energy from 4 to 9/10, stress from 5 to 7/10 and getting on with his sister from 1 to 5/10. Mum wrote a letter and confirmed that John was back in school full time. School was delighted and reported he had caught up. John had done some travelling and was no longer travel sick, and reported having new friends and interests.

Clare (8). Despite Clare having a near phobia of trying new foods, within two months and three sessions she said Sleep had improved from 2 to 6/10, confidence from 3 to 7/10 and anger 4 to 8/10.

Parent's Letter after treatment for ME/Chronic Fatigue Syndrome

Dear Clover Houe,

My son John was 14 and very unwell. It came out of the blue as he was a teenager who did rugby, air cadets and scouts. We could pin point when it started, it was Easter, he was car sick for the first time, and it kept continuing. He would do things but feel really unwell afterwards. No energy, complaining that he felt ill, stomach ache, sore throat, but it would not go away.

We went to the doctor who did blood tests, which came back negative. They said that it was a virus. John got worse to the point he could no longer go to school, he became very withdrawn. We hoped that over the summer holidays he would get better, but it made no difference, in fact he was getting worse, not having the energy to do anything.

As a parent it was frustrating when he would not listen to me. I would ask him to just walk around the block or eat more nutritious meals. But he would not listen. It became very stressful for the whole family. After numerous visits to the Doctors they decided to refer him to a consultant, as they thought he could have chronic fatigue syndrome (CFS). We had to wait a further three months to see a consultant. John was now going into Year 10. When we finally saw the consultant they also thought he had CFS, but had to do more tests and would see him in two months time, which was very frustrating because we wanted answers. In the meantime a friend suggested Clover House.

We went to see the staff at Clover House, in the hope of finding a solution to John's illness. It was a very relaxed atmosphere. They took time to find out what sort of person he was and how we worked as a family. The imagery therapist listened to us both, as life had become so stressful. She talked about how we both should work through things.

The nutritionist really explained to John what a difference a change in his diet could do. Being a teenager his diet was not very good, and he would not listen to his mother! She also recommended different supplements.

We then saw a lady who gave John a massage, which he found very relaxing as he was very stressed. Each therapist gave us advice on things we could do at home.

We both took Clover House's advice, and with the supplements recommended, John started to make a recovery. Slowly but surely he was getting stronger. Within five months of going to Clover House, John had returned to school full time.

I cannot tell people what a relief it was to see my son back as he was. The stress of those eight months was horrible. When your child is normally fit and healthy but suddenly becomes so ill that they can no longer lead a normal life it is horrible.

We went back to the consultant who said he could not explain it, but John was back to normal, and it was some kind of virus.

For anyone whose child is unwell to the point that they cannot go to school, or their behaviour is no longer classed as normal, I would recommend a visit [to Clover House]. They understand what you as a parent and your child are going through. They take a holistic approach and look at everything about your child, not just the symptoms. It worked for us.

Chapter 27

Panic Attacks

Scores for children suffering panic attacks averaged out at commencement 2.25 / 10 and improved to 7.3 / 10 in an average of three sessions.

The Problems

Emma aged 10 had experienced anxiety and panic attacks which, her mother wrote, was probably 'from the last school year with a teacher who was very harsh and bullied the children to get them to toe her line. Emma was very frightened of her and was not attending school, all her confidence was sapped and she became more and more dependent on me.' They had seen the GP, a consultant paediatrician, and a psychiatrist.

She also reported that Emma couldn't get to sleep and woke up during the night. At their first session we noticed that Emma was pale with dark shadows under her eyes, had lost a lot of weight and had stomach aches.

David aged 9 was unable to go to school because of anxiety and panic attacks. He had also given up Cubs and football. He had been having the panic attacks for a year, when he was bullied at school by some older boys. He had a fear of being sick, and often thought he was feeling unwell. He also found it difficult to go into his own bedroom alone, and slept with his mother while his father slept in his bed.

He had become increasingly anxious and worried about germs and was constantly washing his hands. They had been to the doctor and to the Child and Adolescent Mental Health Service (CAMHS) but the situation had not improved.

Elizabeth aged 18 had been recommended to Clover House by a friend, and her mother had written a note explaining that two years previously Elizabeth had had a relationship with a boy and then had disclosed she had been self harming, was struggling at school and her boyfriend was being unkind to her.

They had been to the doctor and school tutors. Her mother was spending several nights sleeping with her in her room as she was having panic attacks at night, and they had been to see a counsellor at the hospital. The counsellor had said that she needed to work harder at school to get A grades, after which Emma struggled even more. It had all become so much that she could not talk about any of the issues, school, work, boyfriend, or her future.

Nutrition

Emma (10) was not eating regularly, having large gaps without food. We gave her advice about blood sugar imbalances, and how not eating would make her worse. She was asked to eat more fruit, and to have a bowl of cereal before bed as well as at breakfast. We also asked her to include fish in her diet, and to stop orange juice. At the second session Emma was enjoying food again, and eating fish, also enjoying nuts and pumpkin seeds.

David (9) had a varied diet, with plenty of vegetables, but tended to have sugary cereals for breakfast and sugary snacks throughout the day. We explained how stabilising blood sugar levels at breakfast and throughout the day would make him feel mentally stronger. He was asked to swap his cereal to egg on toast and diluted apple juice, to double the filling in his sandwiches, and to have pitta bread and hummus after school. We also said a bedtime snack of cheese and crackers should help him sleep better. Home-made low-sugar cakes and biscuits would also help, and an Epsom salts bath every night would help him relax.

At the second session it was suggested he has a protein breakfast every morning (not just a few times) and to have cheese and crackers rather than cheese dippers.

Elizabeth (18). We had a long discussion about Elizabeth's aches and pains, and about her coming off contraceptive pills. Supplements of B complex for the day and magnesium at night were prescribed. At her second session we had another long talk about foods. We continued motivation and support at the third session, and said to continue with supplements.

Massage

Emma (10). We showed Emma's mother massage techniques to use at home, especially at bedtime to help her sleep. Massage oils and a handout were given to use at home.

David (9). Massage techniques were demonstrated to David's mother and father to continue at home. Later we introduced the metamorphic technique (a light stroking

and tapping on the head), and flower remedies were made
for David and his mother. Mum was worried about his
results slipping, but we reminded her that you often get
what you think, to be aware of this and remain positive.

Elizabeth (18) came with her father to the first session,
and chatted about horses. She was given a foot massage
which she enjoyed and her father practised it too. Even
though he was reluctant at first, they both seemed to enjoy
it and she gave him 9/10. He said it was the first time he
had touched her feet since she had been in nappies. We
gave them massage oils and a handout so that they could
continue at home. Massage techniques were shown to
Elizabeth's mother at the next session.

Imagery

Emma (10). After we had established a good rapport
with Emma, we did a 'rewind' (a technique to clear the
emotional element of a memory) regarding her bad teacher
experience. Emma pictured her panic attacks holding her
tummy. This picture was 'blown out' (a technique to clear
habits) until she could not see original picture any more.
The teacher experience was tested at the second session –
and produced a smile.

More work was done on school, and 'thinking about
tomorrow' as a more useful way of imagining school. We
helped her to switch her language from, 'I have got to do
this,' which made her feel bad, to 'I want to get things
done.'

David (9) described his panic attacks throughout his
whole body, with legs shaking, all hot in the head, feeling

weird and scared he would be sick. He saw it all as being red, but was able to change it to the colour purple. He then imagined his happy/special place as a sandy beach with his family in a cove with grass at the back. Discussion took place with all the family. At the second session, having established his basic fears, 'rewinds' were done on three incidents of sickness.

Elizabeth (18). Elizabeth's father mentioned a car crash that had upset her. She worked on her own and did three 'rewinds' on the car crash, and the deaths of her grandfather and grandmother. We introduced the set of Babushka dolls and explained that. A 'blow out' was done on her panic attacks.

At the next session more 'rewinds' were done on other subjects (that did not need to be disclosed), and she practised doing her own rewinds herself. We asked her to do them on anything she thought about during the coming weeks. She then built up an idea of how the 'new' Elizabeth would look and sound and what she would feel like. She got into the part of Elizabeth at the moment, and 'swished' (a technique for replacing a better picture over an upsetting picture), bringing in the new Elizabeth and out with the old.

We started on a short 'autobiography', a technique for imagining writing your life story watched by a person who loves you to increase self esteem.) Although she had difficulty finding a time when she felt loved, she accessed some moments.

At the third session she was worried about an uncertain future, so a 'rewind' was done again on the aspects that bothered her, and sounds and feelings were included in the rewinds. We talked about dealing with things as they happened, and she built up an imagery to do this which was then internalised.

Results

Emma (10). After two sessions Emma's mother cancelled the third, saying thank you, it was difficult to get through town, and later wrote 'Thanks again to your therapists for their help and support of Emma, she continues to improve and is attending school more or less full time now.'

They scored sleep from 3/10 at the first session, and 6/10 at the second. Panic attacks improved from 1/10 to 6/10 and frequency of attacks from 5/10 to 7/10.

David (9) also attended for only two sessions because we were approaching the Christmas period. Scores after one session showed sleep improved from 2/10 to 8/10, anxiety about sleeping 4/10 to 7/10, and frequency of washing hands from 1/10 to 9/10.

Elizabeth (18). After three sessions Elizabeth scored school improved from 3/10 to 8/10 and panic attacks improved from 3/10 to 9/10.

Letter from Alison (age 16) after treatment for headaches, anxiety, panic attacks, self harm.
Dear Clover House,

Coming to Clover House and having sessions has been one of the most valuable things I have ever done. I came to Clover House because I was really struggling with my anxiety and I was slow quite a lot of the time. I had severe headaches every day, and it was really getting me down. I was also self-harming at especially low times and constantly tired.

Your nutritionist helped me discover that I had a wheat intolerance, which has completely changed my life as I am much less tired and don't get headaches any more.

I was nervous to meet the imagery man, but I was put at ease straight away and we got on really well. We did so many things that helped me and that I can still use to help when I need it. We worked on a lot of my issues and my anxiety improved drastically, and I no longer have panic attacks as regularly.

I'm much more confident and I don't get as anxious. I am nowhere near as down as I used to be and I have ways of coping with things that I wouldn't have even known about before.

I'm a completely different person, thanks to all those who helped me at Clover House.

Thank you so much for everything xxxxx.

Chapter 28

Parents' Separation

Scores directly relating to getting along with mother, father and step parents averaged starting at 2.9/10 and finishing at 7.8/10 in an overall average of 3.6 sessions. Other symptoms included sleep problems, anger, lack of concentration, unhappy, aggression, lack of confidence, school problems, bedwetting, tantrums, stress, anxiety, panic attacks, and fitting in. The average score for these additional symptoms began at 2.7/10 improving to 8/10.

Problems

Alan aged 12 had been displaying anxiety and anger since the age of 2 when his parents had separated. His mother wrote that he over-reacted to difficulties, talked of killing himself, and about being fat. He had had a lot of injuries, but nothing could be explained by a neurologist. He scored sleep at 3/10, anger with mother 3/10, anger about school 2/10, and missing Dad 0/10.

Brian aged 5. Brian's mother wrote that his problems were anger and bad behaviour at home and at school, with poor listening skills. In fact Brian was struggling with his mother and father's separation. School had labelled him difficult and aggressive. Mother had suffered from post-natal depression, and been hospitalised twice.

Father reported that he could not sleep and was inclined to depression. Brian spent Mondays and Thursdays with his father, Tuesdays and Wednesdays with his mother, and alternated weekends of Friday, Saturday and Sunday between the two.

Ella aged 6. Ella's mother had been given our leaflet by her divorce solicitor. She reported that Ella had become 'disruptive and aggressive at home and seemed generally confused and upset about the situation.' She was also distressed on returning from visiting her father, and had severe temper tantrums and got easily upset by the slightest thing for the few days following.

Nutrition

Alan (12) was keen on food, and liked cooking at home. He said he ate well but had lots of junk food in between, and especially after school. He said he nearly always missed breakfast and did not eat his packed lunch.

His mother was vegetarian and hardly ever had fish. His grandmother cooked a roast dinner twice a week for him.

Alan asked lots of questions about healthy foods. Homework was to keep a food diary; read the handouts given; to have breakfast; eat more healthy snacks; have soup or toast after school; to avoid glucose sports drinks, and to eat fish. Supplements of magnesium and fish oil were given.

At the next session we discussed glucose drinks and sports foods, as he was interested in sports. He worried about his weight and getting fat, and he and his mother compromised on his bedtime. We talked about the situation with mother and father, continued into the fourth session.

Brian (5) opened up and talked about his toy guinea pig, Mr Shy. He said Mummy and Daddy lived in separate houses. His mother admitted that she smacked him when he was naughty, and that was why he smacked his toys.

We gave Mum lots of handouts and some advice on how to deal with Brian when angry. Homework was to implement a star chart for eating fish, and for both parents to take more responsibility for decisions about food.

We also advised Mum not to treat Brian as a friend, and to keep a food diary. She had done this for the next session a week later, and Brian had earned five stars. He suddenly burst into tears saying that Daddy was ill. After some coaxing, he said he wanted Daddy to be happy and that Daddy never smiled. Together they set up a star chart for Daddy to get 20 stars for smiling.

Ella (6) generally had a good diet, but we explained that the emphasis needed to be on foods containing magnesium and B vitamins, and help balance blood sugar levels. We emphasised that Ella needed to eat more vegetables and fruit, and have a small snack before bedtime to help her sleep through the night. Breakfast should be more substantial and more protein based.

We encouraged her to try new foods: oily fish, hummus, seeds and lots of new vegetables. As mother seemed stressed, this would also help her. At the second session they had still not had protein for breakfast so we asked them to try beans on toast, egg on toast, or oily fish.

Junior magnesium and B vitamins were given. At the third session it was reported that mother had been ill, so Ella had been making her own breakfast and washing up. She had tried five other vegetables and was encouraged to eat roast chicken not chicken nuggets, and to put extra vegetables on pizza.

Massage

Alan (12) and his mother had a general chat about massage and how it could be helpful. Alan had a foot massage and his mother was keen to help; Alan relaxed.

Homework was to incorporate foot massage into their evening routine, and we gave them massage oils, a handout and a flower remedy sheet. Alan reported enjoying massages at the next session. We demonstrated back massage moves to Mum and reminded her to keep the movements nice and slow.

At the third session Alan said he often argued with his mother in the evenings and then did not want massage. A flower remedy form was completed.

At his fourth session, Alan described the atmosphere with his mother as being tense. She was asked if she was able to do nice things for herself, but replied that she didn't have time and felt lonely. So a flower remedy was done for mother. Alan suggested she joined a salsa dancing class.

Brian (5). Both parents came to the sessions with Brian, and they could see how massage could be helpful to him. Foot massage was demonstrated and some moves on his back and shoulders. At one point both mother and father were massaging Brian's feet and he seemed to enjoy it.

Homework was to try and incorporate massage into bedtime routine as much as possible. At further sessions Brian eagerly ran into the room and jumped on the massage couch, closed his eyes and visibly relaxed.

Ella (6). Ella and her mother each did their own flower remedy, and we showed them some massage techniques. They were given massage oil and handouts to use at home.

At the next session, mother reported doing well with massage and that they had both benefited. We did a quick head, neck, arm and foot massage for Ella. Because of mum's illness no massage was done at home, so they did some more at the third session.

Imagery

Alan (12). The dice magic trick went down well, and quickly led to doing a 'rewind' (a technique to clear the emotional element of a memory) on his parents splitting up about age two. He said he felt better. A grief clearing technique was done on not seeing his father, and we also helped him visualise seeing his father in the future, and Dad waiting for him every day, so that Alan knew he will see him again.

After Alan confirmed he awoke with bad dreams, we asked who could help him in his dreams, and he replied that he needed a team. So a 'dream team' of eleven, and a 'dream arm' were used to help him fall asleep more easily.

At the second session Alan said his thoughts about his Dad had improved, but he was still sad. He was asked to think about this and to become aware of a sad image involving his Dad. Then we did a 'blow out' (a technique to clear a memory) on this and he reported feeling better about it.

At the third session we talked about not having heard from his father. Bedtime was an issue with his mother, so we helped them compromise. At the fourth and final session we used a 'writing your life story' technique, and the lioness, (imagining having the power of a lioness behind you) for confidence, which he was asked to practise. His mother also had some help to 'rewind' events of her father's death at age 11, and the breakup with Alan's father.

Brian (5) was shown a magic dice trick and how to do it himself. As Brian was happy playing on the swing, his parents talked about their depression and trauma, and the 'rewind ' technique was demonstrated. They were asked to use this on everything they could by the next session.

However by next session they had not done so, and it was recorded that two very intense, serious people were perched on the sofa watching Brian play. After playing with Brian he was persuaded to do a 'rewind' on his parents splitting up, making use of crayons as actors, which helped him relax. His father had been on anti-depressants and both parents seem brighter.

After a while Brian said he did not get on with adults at school, so some work was done to help with that.

Ella (6) was introduced to the magic dice trick and a pencil case trick which she enjoyed. We also showed her the set of Babushka dolls, a set of Russian dolls that fitted one inside the other, where the second to last doll has an upset face. We explained the story about how upsetting things can happen but she got over it, which also went down well. Ella strongly agreed that Babushka could help people.

As Ella did not wake up easily in the mornings, a 'dream arm' was installed, and for a super-hero to help in her dreams she chose her mother. Some work was also done with Mum for clearing distressing thoughts and increasing pleasant thoughts.

Another magic trick was shown at the second session. Ella said she did not like dogs, so we talked about dogs, and worked on placing the good thought onto thoughts of dogs.

We introduced Ella to the idea of visualizing herself having a good day, and then seeing herself having a good day in the future. We then returned to today to plan how to get there.

At the third session Ella was asked about the dogs and she shrugged her shoulders and said OK, and mother was enthusiastic about her meeting a dog in the park and stroking it.

She seemed to let her emotions show more in her face and body language, whereas previously she had displayed little emotion. Lastly we talked about things in general, and planning ahead as mentioned previously.

Results

Alan (12). Alan's scores at the fourth session showed that sleep had improved from 2 to 8/10, anger at Mum from 2/10 to 6/10, anger at school 2/10 to 8/10, and missing Dad from 0/10 to 8/10.

Brian (5). Both parents had started to treat their child like a child rather than as a mini-adult. They were very happy and pleased by the fourth session, feeling they had 'Got there'. Brian's teachers and headmaster had commented on his better behaviour.

Dad had earned 30 stars for smiling, and his reward was a trip to the cinema. Scores improved: playing with mummy had gone from 3 to 9/10, responding to instructions 4 to 9/10, playing with Daddy 4 to 9/10 and concentration 4 to 9/10.

Ella (6). Ella's scores had improved, with calm and happy from 5 to 8/10, recognising feelings from 3 to 7/10 and sleep 2 to 7/10. In an evaluation one month later, goals had all been scored at 8/10. Mother wrote she had most liked the 'very child-friendly [attitude], and being welcomed like a family member, being made very comfortable, and all the staff were friendly yet professional.'

Parent's letter after treatment for parents' separation
Dear Clover House,

Sarah had come home from spending some time with her Dad. We had separated, then divorced after I met my new partner. We went away to France, myself, my two daughters and my new partner. We had a nice time, but then lots of problems with Sarah not wanting to do things and being cross with me, which was quite interesting

When we got back Sarah's teacher told me she had been having difficulties with friendships at school and suggested we see the people at Clover House. The teacher said she had become withdrawn, and was hiding sometimes in the class, crouching down on her own. At home if we had a disagreement things were getting a bit out of hand.

I telephoned Clover House and spoke to a really helpful person who took a lot of time to listen to what was going on. They sent me a form to complete about what was happening, which made me think not just about the obvious reasons like her Dad and I no longer living together, but her sister who has disabilities which means she has lots of appointments and operations.

We didn't have to wait long [for an appointment], and I didn't have a clue what was going to happen.

I found the questions challenging, it's realising you can't

cope. It creeps up on you and you feel you should be able to handle it without any help. But Clover House felt non-stigmatising. This wasn't going into therapy for months on end, it was a gentle, holistic approach.

I think some children at Clover House have issues that are clearly related to a poor diet. For us that wasn't the most important element, but John pointed out that it's the combination of therapies which is so powerful.

John the imagery therapist got Sarah imagining how she felt at a particular time, taking herself back, only for a brief moment . . . and click, it was over and they were talking about something else. It was not sitting down and having a long conversation about how you feel.

Because I didn't understand how it works, it did feel quite odd sometimes. I had to go with it and not get too worried about it. I think I had thought that Sarah and her sister seeing their Dad a lot would make it all better and that would be enough, but of course it isn't.

Sarah's sister was used to having appointments and this was Sarah having her appointments, and I'm sure that felt good for her. I couldn't believe we'd be done in four sessions, and yet by the fourth time it felt right that it should be the last one. Now we have days when Sarah can be stroppy with me, and I can be stroppy with her, but the problems have shrunk to a small amount of her life instead of taking over. And I can put proper boundaries around behaviour, without feeling guilty. It's helped me get past a lot of my feelings about the separation, but the main benefit is seeing Sarah happy.

Chapter 29

School Problems

Over 10% of the children coming to Clover House had problems related to school. They ranged from school phobias, school refusals, expulsions, exclusions, anger, aggression, anxieties, bullying, boredom, struggling with school work, trouble mixing with other children, to children being taken to school 'kicking and screaming' and 'still in pyjamas'. The average score for all this started at 3.2/10 and, after an average of 3.4 sessions, improved to 7.6/10.

The Problems

Casey aged 5. Casey's mother wrote that he had been on a fixed term exclusion, and had regularly been excluded and restrained – at least twenty times. 'He had become increasingly angry and violent at school, throwing huge tantrums, trashing the room and losing control,' wrote his mother. When restrained he had begun to bite and spit. His mother also said they had had to employ a solicitor, an independent educational psychologist, speech and language therapist, and a nanny to enable her to work part time.

Eric aged 10. Eric's mother reported some severe symptoms. 'He wrote about wanting to die, he denied or lied about his negative behaviour, is oppositional, defiant, anxious, fidgety, angry, sometimes aggressive, self harming, impulsive, dangerous to self and sometimes to others.' She added that he got upset easily, had low self esteem and confidence. Often uncontrollable at school – he was on the verge of permanent exclusion for the second time – 'so we have withdrawn him.' Eric had experienced some bullying, being punched in the stomach.

Charlie aged 13 had developed a phobia about not being able to go to school. He had been bullied at a previous school, and was having emotional problems. An educational welfare officer had been involved, but Charlie was still scared. He came with his grandmother as he lived with her, and only saw his mother occasionally. His father was letting him down over visiting arrangements.

Nutrition

Casey (5) was constantly demanding during his first session, covering his father's face and screaming No to everything. His parents were asked to fill in a food diary and we gave them handouts on food allergies and healing crisis. We suggested they reduce his milk intake and change from flavoured to plain crisps.

By the second session Casey's mother said it had been mind blowing and amazing. They had changed to goat's milk without him noticing, giving him multivitamins and massaging him with flax oil. By the fourth session Casey knew he should not have chocolate or flavoured crisps and was eating more fruit and vegetables.

Eric (10). After chatting with Eric we learned that he wanted to be a footballer and so was interested in hearing about nutrition and healthy eating, which was necessary for anyone to become a successful, injury-free footballer. We gave them several handouts and recipes. Homework was to avoid oranges, orange juice and apples, replacing them with bananas and kiwi fruit. We also asked him to complete a star chart, and to earn at least 14 stars by eating different sorts of fish and vegetables. Also to have supper at bedtime, keep a food diary, take magnesium at night and Omega oils after school.

His parents were very keen and supportive and reported good progress, they had taken all advice on board. We asked them to carry on with the food diary and star chart, and to stop pesto sauce. We suggested that in order to calm down after sport, Eric should not go on the computer, but have quiet time and a bath.

We advised keeping up the food diary for the next six months, and using the star chart for other good behaviours such as listening to relaxing music at bedtime. We also encouraged him to put his thoughts into a dustbin at bedtime, saying goodnight to his problems and worries.

Charlie (13). A long list of homework included no pot noodles, crisps, fizzy drinks, or chocolate. We strongly recommended introducing brown rice, plenty of different coloured vegetables, oily fish (sardines, tuna, salmon), and red meat once a day, and no smoked foods.

We asked him to eat two bowls of cereal a day, but no added sugar; to have only one spoonful of sugar in his tea, not two.

After school he should have two pieces of wholemeal bread, lots of nuts, and at least two apples a day. Also to include B vitamins and magnesium supplements at night.

Refinements to his diet made later included fruit juice to be from cartons, not bottles or tins; to try other fruits; using buckwheat flour to make pancakes, and continue reducing sugar and additives. At the third session Charlie was shown how to use a paper bag for breathing into for panic attacks.

Massage

Casey (5) was still screaming No to everything, probably because of all the things done to him, including lots of hospital tests. He sat on his father's lap, during which we gave Dad a hand massage in order to introduce them both to massage, and massage oils to try at home. His parents reported doing some massage every night, and he was sleeping through. We did some massage for Casey during sessions and he seemed to recognise his need for it as he told his mother he didn't want it on Saturday night because he wasn't going to school, but asked for it on Sunday night.

Eric (10). We explained to Eric that massage is used in football for the relief of tired feet and muscles. A walnut flower remedy for changes was given to help him as he had recently changed to a third school. We demonstrated foot massage and both mother and father practised. Eric enjoyed it and became relaxed. More massage techniques were shown and his parents reported that they used it when they felt he needed it. A full flower remedy was given too. We also suggested headphones to help him relax because Eric complained the house could be quite noisy at bedtime.

Charlie (13). We demonstrated massage techniques to Charlie's grandmother, who was happy to try it at home. We suggested doing it three or four times a week, and for

Charlie not to watch the TV for at least 30 minutes before going to sleep, and to perhaps try listening to music instead. More massage was done at further sessions.

Imagery

Casey (5). So that his parents could talk, Casey was allowed to watch a children's video, which unfortunately made him think that the reason for coming to Clover House was to watch videos. We therefore suggested he take them home to watch. He wanted to see some magic tricks. However, everything we suggested was rejected with screams of No, and throwing things. Asking him to scream and shout – which stopped him – the session ended. We gave him a book, 'The Warm Fuzzy Tale', to take home too.

At the next session we mirrored his body language to gain rapport, and he gradually allowed more contact. He did say 'bye bye' loudly. We discussed things with his parents because most of the time Casey did not want to engage. We praised his parents on his increasing improvement.

Eric (10) had just started his third school a few days previously and had already been in trouble. He said he was being tickled first, and was only responding by 'doing it back to them.' Again his interest in football was used and how Wayne Rooney could do stupid things if riled.

'Anchors' were set on learning football and on learning at school, and then merged. While we talked with his parents, Eric was swinging on the back of the sofa. Dad stopped him. So Eric was asked if he was bored, to which he nodded. He was asked to get that feeling back, and the 'picture' was 'locked', and dragged past his right ear. Asked to get the picture back again, he couldn't do it.

At the second session we talked about how Eric played with older boys, annoying them until they got him to do things when he was likely to get caught. So we used role play and practised other responses such as, 'After you' if he was given a dare.

Because he could not sit still, we did a 'compulsion blow out' (to clear habits) on the idea of fidgeting, and gave him an image of himself feeling more relaxed and calm. When we checked at the next session Eric said he ignored the dares, and we rehearsed other responses.

He was asked to think about something in the future and he saw it in the third person. This was praised and he was shown how to do it in the first person for a moment, which he tried. At the fourth and final session, we discussed confidence and the 'lioness' was installed, imagining being a lioness, or having one behind him for confidence, which he agreed to practise and play with, until he did it well.

Charlie (13). After talking about the bullying, Charlie imagined watching his younger self being bullied and then reliving it backwards at high speed – a rewind. Then, when he thought about school, he brightened up and smiled. He was asked to think about himself doing something in the future and watching himself when he was older succeeding in the future.

Granddad had been helping to look after him and Charlie was asked to imagine finding three ways to take more responsibility for himself. Grandmother also did this, to find ways for Charlie to help himself more.

At the second session Charlie reported being upset over the death of a pet dog six months previously so a 'grieving' process was completed.

Work on bullying included Charlie becoming a sparrow hawk with pickachow powers coming into Charlie to take on the sparrow hawk's strength. At the third session Charlie had seen a TV programme about a ouija board and he had been flooded with unhappy memories of his cat who had disappeared on bonfire night five years ago. Again we did a grief resolution process with him, and Charlie thought about someone he had successfully mourned, and moved Smokey the cat into the same 'place'. On checking it seemed he was OK about both animals.

Results

Casey (5). Mum wrote a letter to us two months later. She had originally written that her son had been 'broken' by the educational system, which had left them with quite a disturbed little boy, and that the drug Ritalin had been the next option. They scored anxiety/stress improved from 1 to 10/10, and evaluated our service at 10/10, having achieved 'a chance to tell their story'. Their child had become calmer almost immediately and was now free of his anger and fear of adults, and was a happy, well-balanced boy again.

'It's a miracle,' wrote Mum. 'Thank you.'

Eric (10). After the first session Eric and his parents reported great progress. The teachers in his new school reported him being a pleasure to teach, and behaving well. His scores improved from 4 to 8/10, personal boundaries from 3 to 8/10, and bedtime 5 to 7/10. His father, who worked as a head teacher, was so impressed with NLP that he began training in order to do it himself. He popped in six months later to say that Eric had had his end of year report. 'All good, not a bad thing in it. He's caught up two years in just three months since coming to Clover House, and he's all set for secondary school.'

Charlie (13). By the second session Charlie was sleeping better, was not so tired, and had hardly any panic attacks. He scored sleep improved from 0 to 6/10, and panic attacks from1.5 to 6/10.

Two years letter during a telephone evaluation, his grandmother scored school at 9/10, sleep and panic attacks at 9/10, and said Charlie was attending college a year early. He loved his massage and still asked for it, and even though the nutrition was difficult at first, it had helped. They had all become more communicative and she was 'very happy with the way things had turned out.'

Parent's letter after treatment for problems at school
Dear Clover House,

I am writing to let you know our new address and also to tell you how Max is getting along. We moved house on Tuesday, and in the few days since then there has been a remarkable change in Max's behaviour. He is calmer and happier and yesterday decided that he wanted to go back to school. He was very scared, but faced his fears and came home totally delighted with his own courage and confidence. He is now looking forward to going back on Monday.

I want to thank you for your help in this, for Max and myself, and for your kindness and understanding. Please thank Jill and Carole for their help also. You all do wonderful work and I'll always be grateful for the care we received at Clover House.

Chapter 30

Separation Anxiety

The average score for separation anxiety at commencement was 2.6/10 and improved to 9.5/10 within an average of three sessions. Other symptoms included poor sleep, school problems, lack of confidence, unhappy, and friends, the average score of which commenced at 2.7/10 and improved to 7.6/10.

The Problems

Julian aged 14. Julian's mother wrote a note explaining that he was unable to sleep away from home on his own, and that his anxiety resulted in severe symptoms of stomach ache, vomiting, headaches and panic attacks, which meant he was unable to participate in social and school activities. He never had friends over to stay. They sought our help because it was compulsory that he attend a residential trip for all Year 9 pupils at school involving four nights away from home.

Beth aged 9 had a list of problems: unhappy, overweight, aggressive, lack of friends, and clingy. She still needed a dummy, and slept in her parents' bedroom (half a metre away from mother). She was unable to go on sleepovers, even visits to her grandmother were difficult. She worried if her mother had to go out, being anxious for days and became hysterical. They had tried babysitters but she stayed awake until her parents came back, and got herself into a state. She worried about 'things' crawling over her, and was terrified of going to bed or to sleep.

Paul aged 12. Paul's mother wrote that he did not like to spent time away from his parents and even at school he phoned or texted them several times a day. He had a real fear that something would happen when he was away from his parents. He also had a lack of confidence, was worried about his weight, and had an attitude towards his sister and father. He was also struggling at school and developing tics and twitching.

Nutrition

Julian (14). We explained to Julian how eating sweet foods and refined cereals would affect his mood and increase any anxious tendencies. We also explained how his blood sugar balance and diet could be altered to provide more stable and balanced levels. Changes included his breakfast to muesli, trying natural bio-yoghurt, and changing his evening snack from a banana to a wholemeal peanut butter and banana sandwich. We also asked him to increase fluids. Supplements of magnesium and B vitamins were prescribed.

At the second session most of the suggested changes had been made. At the third session the family scored themselves 9/10 for their efforts with nutrition.

Beth (9) liked her food, but she was being called fat at school. It seemed portions were rather large. So after discussion we recommended reducing portion sizes, having an apple mid morning, no jaffa cakes, fish two to three times a week, and some supper to stabilise blood sugar levels throughout the night. We advised her to eat slowly and to chew her food thoroughly. We also asked her to keep a food diary. At the second session Beth had stopped having seconds for school dinners. She would not take supplements so we changed them to a liquid formula. Further motivation was given during her next session.

Paul (12) was found to have a diet high in junk food, refined carbohydrate, sweets and fizzy drinks. He did not like fruit or vegetables. We recommended him to control his blood sugar balance in order to help him feel stronger and to improve concentration. We told him the best way to do this was to avoid junk foods and sweets, replacing them with fruit, water and homemade cakes, which would also help his weight. Swapping chocolate cereals to bacon and eggs on wholemeal toast would help too, as would having chicken in sandwiches, and an apple on the way home from school.

We also suggested that Paul went shopping and became more involved in the selection of foods and trying them. Also to increase his walking to and from school; join a martial arts class to improve confidence and exercise; and join a sports team at school. We gave him a blood sugar handout.

By the second session Paul had been having more protein breakfasts, his mother had made cakes, the family had changed from white to wholemeal and brown rice, pasta, etc.; and he had tried five different fruits. He was feeling better and was given a reminder not to go without breakfast, and to keep increasing his exercise levels.

Massage

Julian (14) was worried about massage, so we demonstrated a foot massage, and his mother was given some massage oils, a booklet and a handout to continue at home. A flower remedy sheet was also given. Some head massage was shown and the flower remedy was completed.

Beth (9). Beth's mother enjoyed trying massage, although Beth was quite ticklish. They were asked to do massage at home as much as possible and had some oils and a handout. They reported at the next session that they were both enjoying massage at home. We demonstrated reflexology (foot massage) including areas of the foot corresponding with calming and relaxing. Her mother reported that talking about parenting issues helped her too.

Paul (12). After hearing Paul's scores, we suggested he do some activities and complete them successfully, instead of opting out. We showed him foot massage, and gave him massage oils, and handouts. Massage was shown again at the second session, which both Paul and his parents enjoyed. We also suggested letting Paul have more of a voice as he was growing up.

Imagery

Julian (14). In discussion Julian described his early experiences of staying away from home. In Year 5 he had been on a two-day school trip which was OK, but on two further trips some people were not nice. We introduced the Babushka dolls, (a Russian doll set where the second to last doll has an upset face, and a story told how things happened and she got over it.)

We moved on to crayons, building a framework of what had happened on a Cub camp and then did 'a rewind' (a technique to clear the emotional element of a memory). Julian then said he would like more confidence, and we worked on that, seeing himself succeeding in the future.

At the second session he was asked to think about sleeping away from home and allowing the fear to develop. We used an 'arm technique' similar to 'dream arm' to really get into this, and he changed the colour scheme to green/yellow. A 'sticky arm' technique was used to substitute confidence about sleeping away. Lastly the 'lioness' technique (imagining being a lioness protecting her cubs) was used, which he enjoyed. We asked him to practise all this as often as possible. Further work on confidence was done at the third and last session.

Beth (9) talked about being overweight. She said she'd always been fat and remembered being called 'fatty' on her first day of school. So a 'rewind' was completed on this. She was helped to clear unpleasant feelings when thinking about herself at school, and seeing herself in the future.

Beth was reluctant to deal with sleep. Mother suggested having a new room, newly decorated, and a 'rewind' was done on her new room, and work on changing 'feeling safe' from 'feeling scared in my room'. We also used stories about growing up or being left behind.

Sleeping arrangements were changed, with Beth sleeping in the room next to her parents on the top bunk bed, with mother in the lower bed. When she was asleep, her youngest brother was put in the lower bed.

We worked again on Beth being on her own. We asked her to imagine going alongside the future to a time when she would be on her own, and pop back and forth to remember how easy it was. At the fourth and final session Beth wanted to work on some upsetting incidents at school. 'Rewinds' were done (without describing what these incidents were).

Paul (12) first did his special place (a big house, garden, nice, clean and tidy). As he was constantly telling himself he was fat, this was changed to a time-line progression where he saw an image of himself as a reasonable build, muscular (but not excessive) and doing some exercise.

We discussed what he 'gained' by being argumentative with his father on school mornings, which he agreed was nothing. We also spoke about his sister instigating arguments, and he came to the conclusion that it would be more beneficial for him not to argue and see how that improved the situation.

Mum was able to see that the house and their actions were untidy and chaotic, and to introduce more guidelines and boundaries, with his sister going to bed earlier than Paul, which would give him some quality time.

Paul had overheard his mother having a telephone conversation about a bad accident (she is a Police officer) and a 'rewind ' was done.

He explained too about his school experiences at age 4, when he would cry and cling to his mother not to leave, and recalled a teacher shouting at him to get back into the classroom. He had found it difficult to go to Cub camp, and was afraid about the next one coming up. Rewinds were done on these negative school experiences, and we helped him remember having fun with two of his friends instead.

Results

Julian (14). Within one month and at the third session scores had improved for sleep from 1 to 6/10, confidence from 2 to 7/10 and sleepovers from 1 to 9/10. One month later his mother wrote an email saying sleepovers were 10/10 and sleep-ins 10/10 after having a sleep-in, and going on the school trip. She wrote, 'This is a great success, and we are all so pleased we found you.'

Beth (9). Within 4 sessions Beth was sleeping on her own. They scored sleep improved from 1 to 10/10, weight improved from 3 to 9/10. In an evaluation her mother most liked 'the focus on Beth was kind and helpful. The whole family of four had benefited, being able to sleep alone and had gone away on a class retreat. We were very proud of her and she was very proud of herself. Thank you, she would not have managed this without your help.'

Paul (12) had just two sessions. By the second session it was reported he had more energy, could concentrate more and his school work had improved. The family reported better routines and a calmer atmosphere. His scores were weight improved from 5 to 7/10, school from 5 to 8/10, independence from 4 to 6/10 and happy from 5 to 8/10.

After an email to see if they wanted a third session his mother said all was good, all scores had improved further and he had said he was 10/10 happy.

Chapter 31

Sibling Rivalry

C hildren came with a variety of problems connected to sibling rivalry. Those that scored this problem specifically averaged 2.5/10 at commencement, improved to 7/10 after an average of 3 sessions. Other symptoms improved from 3/10 to 8/10.

The Problems

Mandy aged 8 came to Clover House because she had had been getting tummy aches for four years. Although she had been to hospital twice, the results were inconclusive. Her mother was concerned that she was a little overweight, and had some eczema. She mentioned that a foster child had been introduced into the family. Initial scores were 5/10 for tummy aches, 5/10 for foster sister and 3/10 for eczema. During their sessions it was disclosed that father had left the family but Mandy had not been told.

Rachel aged 9 was introduced by a friend and her mother had written that her daughter 'was very angry, could not control her temper, and could not accept any telling off.' She told her mother she hated her several times a day, and was constantly fighting with her older sister. Dad had said he had a stressful job and wanted to come home to a peaceful house without all the shouting.

Rachel watched TV in bed until 9.30 pm every night and did not sleep well. It was also recorded that Rachel's school friends called her fat and stupid.

Emma aged 9 was 'very angry and very controlling, mainly to her younger brother.' Her mother also wrote that Emma's self esteem was low and she was constantly seeking reassurance. Her mother and father had divorced and Emma had taken it badly, still wanting her parents to be a family. This had been going on for a couple of years. She was also biting her nails and sucking her thumb.

Nutrition

Mandy (8). After discussion on Mandy's four-day food diary, and getting to understand Mandy's favourite foods and dislikes, the first session homework was to reduce wheat, cut out oranges, orange juice, and fizzy drinks. Also to cut down on tomatoes and eggs. Although Mandy already had soya milk instead of cow's, she was still having yoghurt and cheese every day and was asked to reduce this.

We gave them handouts, and they reported improvements at the next session two weeks later, and all homework had been done. We talked about portion control and gave general motivation to continue with the changes.

Rachel (9). Both parents had a long session, aware that nutrition was a huge contributory factor to Rachel's behaviour, but they did not know how to tackle it. They often gave in for a quiet life, as there would be huge arguments if they tried to enforce regulations or guidelines. We explained that erratic blood sugar levels could be a major factor and how certain foods and drinks exacerbate irritability.

We suggested a non-confrontational approach should be taken, explaining quietly why certain foods were better for her, rather than demanding she ate them. We also explained that a taste for different foods needed to be developed over many attempts. Advice included having brown bread not white, to avoid white flour products, and use wholemeal flour for cooking. Pizza should be a treat only, and they should continue reducing sugar and additives. Multi-vitamin supplements were given.

At the second session, we recommended Rachel to have two bowls of cereal a day (one of which should be porridge) and no sugar on cereals. We asked Mum to make home-made soups. We began to establish rapport with Rachel, she was aware she was on the chubby side and being ridiculed at school.

We spent plenty of time discussing with her how foods were making her react, and which foods she was willing to try. We encouraged her to make her own flapjacks, rather than eating cakes and biscuits. We assured her Omega fish oils would aid concentration, help the endocrine system and her blood sugar levels. We advised her that this long-term enjoyable eating plan was a way of life, not a diet.

Further advice at the third and final session included trying buckwheat flour from health food shops for pancakes and pizza, and to try other flours. Also to try a juicer.

Emma (9). Overall Emma's eating was very good and she liked roast dinners and vegetables. The only food she did not like was mushrooms, but she liked jaffa cakes and cola. Homework was to buy meat from the butchers, no cakes (including jaffa), and no sugar treats after 4 pm. We asked her to do a star chart for drinking water, and asked her to earn at least 14 stars. We also recommended they batch-bake food for the freezer, and a fruit cake for after school.

At the second session Emma's mother reported they had made an apple pie together, and that she was keeping an eye on labels. Emma was interested in foods, understood and took on board our advice. However she craved sweets, so we suggested they make homemade sweets together which would avoid additives, which went down well.

Massage

Mandy (8). First we showed Mandy some foot massage, and then some further massage techniques, which mother was keen to learn and did well. Although Mandy was chatty she found it hard to make eye contact, and we told her mother that doing some massage would help Mandy's body image and self-awareness. At the second session, having reported they had done three or four massages at home, we demonstrated extra moves for the stomach area. They seemed loving towards each other and enjoyed massage. We gave them a music CD for relaxation.

Rachel (8) loved having massage and was very keen for her mother to do this every night. We gave practical advice on cutting back on the TV in her bedroom and to quieten her mind before sleep. We also advised her parents to present a united front, to ignore the bad and praise the good. Massage moves were practised and Rachel enjoyed it.

Emma (9). We established rapport with Emma by talking about dogs. Her mother had done a sports massage course and given occasional massages. We showed them a foot massage and Mum continued. Emma relaxed and gave her mother 10/10. We therefore encouraged them to do some foot massage at home.

At the second session we discussed the family's proposed house move, and how things would be better when Emma had her own room. Emma enjoyed massages and her mother agreed to start making more free time to spend with her.

Imagery

Mandy (8). Magic tricks caught Mandy's attention and helped establish good rapport. We introduced her to the set of Babushka dolls, one with an upset face, and a story that upsetting things happen do happen but then get better.

We discussed how Mandy felt towards Susie, the foster child, and did some rewinds (clearing the emotional elements of memories). We used other methods on two different aspects about Susie.

Finally Mandy was told about the mountain lioness and how to get inside her and feel powerful. We practised the lioness technique at the second session. Mandy said she still had unpleasant feelings in her tummy, especially when worried. When we asked the colour of this feeling she said it was black or purple. So we told her a story that ended with all the purple balloons (her bad feelings) floating up and away for ever.

We showed her how to imagine herself in the future, arriving just after an event happened about which she had felt apprehensive. We then brought her back to the present, and taught her that now she no longer needed to feel apprehensive. She tried it out and was asked to keep using this technique.

She was also asked to imagine a 'disassociated' future rather than an 'associated' one, to which she again immediately responded.

At the third and final session Mandy had been told by her mother about her separation from her father. Through discussion we found Mandy had guessed there was something unusual going on. She was asked to imagine the whole thing at a distance and relived the whole separation backwards. We then helped her picture a future with her mother, with lots of hugs.

Rachel (8) was introduced to the Babushka dolls, and shown how the doll's life resembled hers. We discussed how nice it would be if she could handle 'No' and she imagined seeing herself a day older, getting a 'No' answer and dealing with it beautifully. This older Rachel was very pleased with herself. She also imagined being older and feeling really good, we helped her imagine the scene again.

At the second session, Rachel said she did not like school. She liked the Maths and Science teachers but did not get on with the History and Geography teachers. When she thought about the Maths and Science teachers, she looked in one direction. Thinking about History and Geography, she looked about 60% further right. So we made it fun to move the History and Geography teachers into the same place she thought about the Maths and Science teachers. (i.e. changing visual sub-modalities).

Rachel then said she did not like doing difficult work, and would not do it. She was helped to imagine what it would be like when she and her friends were five years older, i.e. 14. She looked forward to being 14. We pointed out that her friends would have done all the work asked of them and know the things 14 year olds need to know. But poor Rachel would still be acting like a 9 year old. What would her friends think of her? Rachel was downcast at this, and she then imagined doing the hard work and growing up to be a real 14 year old. She also imagined some of the food she likes and adding foods she doesn't like, and planning to try them too. We used a swish technique to help her stop biting her nails, and there was just time for a story about her sister being the eldest.

For the third session there had been only one upset with her sister about using the computer. After discussion a 'reframe' was done on her sister teasing her, and as a practical idea we suggested keeping a log of computer activity.

Emma (9). We showed Emma a magic dice trick, with comments about how things aren't always what they seem. We followed this with the Babushka dolls.

Emma created a play theatre using crayons to deal with her parents splitting up, with some 'rewinds' to follow. We suggested for homework she should draw a picture for us of something really important. And we made a start on her nail biting.

At the second session she brought her picture of her family, which included her absent father. Everyone was smiling – her brother dominated the picture. Crayons were again used to talk about his arrival in the family, followed by a 'rewind' on this. A 'help frame' was set up for Emma to go back in time and help her younger self through her brother's arrival.

At her third session on imagery, Emma attended with her brother. She showed us a drawing she had done of how she stopped quarrelling with him. It was of a lamp with the words 'See the light'. She told us the story behind it, which was that she went to the cinema and saw a film about a girl and her brother, and the girl behaved as Emma did. Suddenly she sees the light and was now able to get on with her brother very well. We asked if this idea could be used for other little girls, to which she agreed.

Because she still missed her father a lot, we worked on moving images of Dad for a better way of thinking about him. For a finale, we used 'Life Story' imagery, which had a notable effect on her, which her mother noticed too.

The Results

Mandy (8). Within one month Mandy's tummy aches, which she had been having for four years, had gone, which she scored 10/10. The score for her foster sister improved to 9/10 and eczema to 8/10.

Mandy and her mother sent us a thank you card saying, 'Thank you for your great advice like the balloons, healthy eating and massages. I really enjoyed my sessions with you all. I am very grateful and it has really helped me.' Mum wrote, 'We both gained an amazing amount of practical tips and hints to help us both.'

Rachel (8). In less than 10 days it was reported that Rachel was so much nicer and kinder. She had started to cook for herself at home and was helping her parents. Her sister came along to the third session because she was amazed how well her sister was behaving. She had even started apologising! Apparently they both went to the cinema with an aunt, who had given them cola, to which they both reacted very badly in mood and temper.

Emma was now sleeping better, was not day dreaming, and was concentrating at school. They had originally scored temper tantrums at 1/10, but after three sessions within one month this had improved to 8/10.

We contacted Mum a year later for evidence of sustained results and she scored tantrums at 10/10. They had gone on holiday abroad which they would never have been able to do previously. She liked that 'it helped all of us.'

Emma (9). Emma had massaged her brother after her first session, and she scored stopping being cross with him from 2/10 improved to 6/10 in just two sessions. Stopping being cross altogether went from 4/10 to 6/10.

In a later evaluation her mother scored aims achieved at 9/10, and satisfied at 10/10. She wrote that it had enabled her to step back and really listen to what her daughter was saying, and to understand her anxieties and insecurities. They had both achieved 'tools' to help, and were able to see how their actions affected others.

Chapter 32

Sleep Problems

Problems with sleep was one of the main symptoms of distress with most children attending Clover House. The average score at commencement was 2.7/10 and improved to 7.9/10. Other symptoms averaged 2.7/10 and improved to 7.8/10.

The Problems

John aged 9 had had difficulty sleeping ever since he started school. His mother said he could not 'switch off', and was awake until 10 or 11pm. He had to be woken for school, and was then tired. They had tried medication from the doctor.

At the first session we found that he had started school at the top grade, but this had since deteriorated, and he said he was getting questions wrong at school because he was tired. He had cried at school because the teacher had shouted. He seemed not to live up to his own expectations and said, 'Daddy wants me to be good at things I can't do.'

Amy aged 8. Amy's mother wrote that Amy had trouble getting to sleep, found it difficult to be alone upstairs at night and sometimes during the day. They had been to the doctor who had said she was probably getting enough sleep, but Mum knew she had bags under her eyes, was tired on waking, and often tearful. She had hesitated for several months over attending Clover House, thinking the problem was not serious enough. Amy and her mother scored sleep at 2/10, confidence 1/10, mother at 6/10 and homework 6/10.

Jack aged 6. Jack's mother wrote that he didn't sleep for the first four and half years of his life. Now he was having night terrors. 'He jumps up, walks around, waving his arms and answers questions, can go to the toilet and have a drink, and looks scared. In the morning he knew nothing about it.' He also had headaches which made him cry. This had been going on for four years. Mum herself had had ill health for the last 18 months.

Nutrition

John (9). Advice at the first session included having to swap his Coco Pops and orange juice breakfast to egg on toast and diluted orange juice, which should help to stabilise his blood sugar levels, and help him concentrate at school. We also suggested he had a mid-morning snack such as carrots, and just to have one sweet food each day. We recommended hummus and pitta bread after school as a snack. We agreed his normal tea was sufficient, but suggested hot chocolate should be changed to dark cocoa powder. We asked John to drink at least 500mls of water throughout the day. Epsom salts baths would help relaxation.

By the second session John had enjoyed egg or beans on toast for breakfast, and been having some seeds for snacks. We suggested adding some natural bio-yogurt with different kinds of fresh fruit.

We recommended magnesium supplements at bedtime when not having an Epsom salts bath. By the third session John had reached drinking his daily quota of water, and had taken on board all nutritional advice. We had further discussion on increasing the variety of foods.

Amy (8) was found to be a fussy eater, and only ate what she wanted, and she had fixed ideas. Her mother had got into the habit of just preparing what Amy wanted. They felt she ate three good meals a day and no snacks.

She appeared tired with no energy, pale with dark rings under her eyes. We informed the family about the importance of less sugar in her diet, and to have a snack in the evening before bedtime, and for Amy to try different fruits and vegetables. We prescribed supplements of Omega 3 fish oils, and junior multivitamins and minerals, and gave them handouts on blood sugar, a new food chart, and ways to encourage Amy to eat more fruit and vegetables.

At the second session we gave the blood sugar explanation again, and discussed trying different ways to cook potatoes other than roast. We gave them some ideas for including protein at breakfast. We asked her mother to get Amy involved in buying and preparing food, for her to see it as normal and fun. They were reminded that foods need to be tried at least five times before accepting them.

Jack (6). At our first brief session with Jack we suggested homework would be to have some supper, and milk in the evenings. The family had discussions to bring them on board for a healthier diet, and they become more positive. We gave them a star chart as well as children's multi-vitamins and mineral supplements.

Massage

John (9). John's mother had given him baby massage, and had had massages herself. She was shown a massage routine and given our booklet and a massage handout, a relaxing CD and a handout on anxiety. A flower remedy sheet was completed, and we showed them the meta-morphic technique (a light tapping and stroking of the head, hands and feet). Mum asked to rehearse 'rocking' the feet backwards and forwards for insomnia.

Amy (8) was quiet but friendly and got on the couch fully dressed to go through a complete massage routine. Her mother said it made her realize that the family is not very relaxed. Father had a stressful job, and she has to cram work into school times. They took home some massage oils, our booklet and a massage handout. At the second session it was said Amy liked her head and ears being massaged and her toes being pulled and rocked. We showed them the metamorphic technique at the following session.

Jack (6) was introduced to massage by a toy monkey. We showed his mother how to give him a foot massage, which Jack really enjoyed. We added positive expectations such as, 'You'll sleep really well after this.' Homework was to continue the massages at home. We also showed his mother how to give a back massage, shoulders, neck and hands, and reminded her to reassure Jack while she was massaging him, and to put his worries to rest.

Imagery

John (9) did his 'special place' (at Judo) as well as one for his mother. We did a 'rewind' (to clear the emotional element) about his teacher who was abrupt and shouted. We found John to be quite negative and worried, so we created a 'What if?' bin, which was black and triangular in shape, as high as his waist, in which to put all his worries and 'What if?' concerns. We made scores on his sister, his father, pressure and sleep.

John's mother discussed some parenting issues with us, and decided on new boundaries, privacy in the bedrooms, and bathroom routines.

At the third session a 'rewind' was done on the previous evening, which had been an exception to his sleeping well.

When we checked, John could still get upset when his teacher shouted, and we found he had forgotten to 'change her clothes, hair colour to ginger, and special glasses with springing eyes.'

He still felt himself under pressure from his father who wanted him 'to do good things' so this was 'reframed' to suggest his father was recognising how well he was doing and wanted him to continue doing well.

Amy (8). We used the magic book to establish rapport with Amy, and in discussion we found she had been frightened by something on television and scared of sleeping ever since. She remembered the incident, and without any details we set up a 'play theatre' with crayons to act out the parts, and did a 'rewind'. She nodded when asked if it had stopped bothering her. To help her sleep 'a dream arm' was installed. Our first session ended with another magic trick.

At the second session we worked on accessing her bad feelings, and we helped her make it larger and brighter and nearer for a 'blow out' technique for clearing habits.

Mum also reported lack of confidence so a friendly version of the lioness technique (imagining having a lioness behind her for confidence) was done, with a request for her to practise this everyday and use it when needed.

At the third session Amy could not remember her issues, and we worked more on self confidence using the 'autobiography' imagery, where she accessed a memory of realising that someone loved her. We then talked about seeing herself in the future; she learned to use the second person perspective when thinking about herself and what she was going to do, and to use the first person position briefly after seeing herself succeed in the future.

Jack (6). After Jack's mother recalled her forceps delivery, we gently suggested the difficult birth may have been the cause of his problems now, and she burst into tears. We did some rewinds and help techniques were used to deal with this. Some magic tricks soon got mother and Jack laughing, and then we showed Jack the Babushka dolls.

At the second session Jack wanted some more magic tricks, which we did for him. He had brought a picture to show us of mother, father and dogs, so we asked him to draw himself in as well. We then asked him why they were not smiling, even though everyone was happier recently. So he changed the faces to happy.

Using crayons we did a rewind to his mother's illness, and we told him several stories about empathy and to notice when his mother is feeling better.

At the third and final session Jack had had an unpleasant dream, so the therapist 'stuck' the dream on the back of his hand, and flipped his palm over it. We asked Jack to imagine a much better dream and this was 'stuck' to the therapists hand. After two or three sequences of hand flipping between the two dreams, and some further stories about how we can step out, change things, and step back in, Jack said he could not remember the old dream.

The Results

John (9). After John's first session he was asleep by 8 pm, and by his third session he reported having more energy in the mornings and waking up by himself.

His scores after two sessions over one month were: sister improved from 4 to 7/10, Dad improved from 6 to 9/10, pressure from 3 to 8/10 and sleep from 1 to 6/10.

Amy (8). By the third session Amy had a completely different outlook on food and eating. She had made a meal for her friend, and wanted to do more cooking. She had tried many different foods, and was found to have the highest aerobic fitness in her class. The teachers had mentioned she looked healthier with no bags under her eyes. Her mother said it had been great to step back and look at what was happening. Amy's scores improved on confidence from 1 to 8/10, Mum from 6 to 8/10, homework from 6 to 8/10 and sleep from 2 to 10/10.

Jack (6) After two sessions, they scored sleep improved from 4 to 8/10 and feeling healthy from 4 to 6/10. All our therapists reported that both Jack and his mother looked happier and healthier.

Parent's Letter after treatment for Sleep and Glue Ear

Dear Clover House,

Simon was basically trouble from the day he was born,

he would never feed properly and he constantly cried all day and night and we could rarely put him down and have a break. His crying was so bad that we constantly took him to the doctor and even the children's hospital in order to find out what was wrong with him.

Simon's temper also left much to be desired and he would always seem so frustrated. We basically didn't get much help from the medical profession – no one really seemed to listen to us or take the matter seriously! The hospital would comment that 'all children cry – it's normal.'

My own doctor told me to leave Simon crying in his cot even when he was biting the cot and covering it with blood. She said, 'Don't worry he won't hurt himself! Why not try putting him in a baby grow which stops him from sitting up and then he won't be able to bite the cot!' This I did not do. She basically said I just had to put up with the constant crying!

It was eventually picked up that Simon was getting constant ear infections, and so was constantly given antibiotics. He could not concentrate at all; he would not play, not watch TV, or listen to music. After noticing one day Simon did not respond when spoken to I was having grave doubts that something was wrong with him, especially when someone noticed Simon lip reading. I once again went off to the doctor and insisted that they refer us to a specialist, which did not go down too well – again they insisted nothing was wrong.

We eventually found out that Simon had had glue ear since birth and his ears where extremely scarred from the many ear infections. The specialist even commented that no wonder Simon was crying, he must have been in such severe pain! As I was pregnant at the time and felt I could not take much more crying and bad behaviour, we went privately and paid for the operation ourselves.

By the age of 18 months Simon was fitted with grommets in both ears. Unfortunately he was one of the children where grommets did not take immediate effect, so the ear infections continued for quite a while after the operation.

As Simon grew, his ear infections improved but not his temper. His behaviour was so bad it was difficult to take him anywhere, especially when he started to get violent towards me. He would hit, bite, kick, pull my hair – he would do anything in a fit of rage. His bad language was also something that completely shocked me!

He would accept no discipline from me whatsoever. If I sent him to bed he would scream, kick and pull the bedroom door, which is now hanging off its hinges, kick the bedroom window with all his might, bite his toys and throw them all around the room. If I tried to leave the room he would hang on to my clothes, hitting me all the while – this could go on for hours. Many times we would just try and hold onto Simon in order to calm him down, but his strength and stamina was amazing and nothing we did or said seemed to help.

Even when I had company things became unbearable. He would throw his table and chairs across the room, constantly scream, kick the patio doors. We tried everything to stop this, from ignoring him completely, smacking him, taking toys away, sending him out of the room, sitting him down, talking to him – all to no avail.

Another example: I took Simon on a boat trip with my family. He was in a bad temper all day and finally flipped when we were in the tea gardens, and chairs and cups of tea went flying everywhere in front of everyone.

Simon also found sleeping a problem. He would go to bed late, get up early and wake up every single night. This continued for years and is now only beginning to settle down. Simon is now nearly 6 and it is only recently that I have been able to stop him sleeping with me all night. As soon as I'd leave his bed he would come to find me.

I finally reached the end of my tether when Simon's behaviour became bad after school. He would kick me in front of his friends. If I said we were going home he would scream and run around the playground.

My husband heard of Clover House through a friend who had been having trouble with his teenager and had been impressed with the results. As we had nothing to lose and knew we could not continue putting up with Simon's behaviour I phoned – relief on the end of the phone – someone seemed to understand at last!

We attended seven sessions at Clover House. They sorted out Simon's diet. Out went rubbish food and in came fruit and vegetables. We found out that Simon was allergic to dairy products. He was given children's vitamins which Simon said helped him with his 'naughtiness'. He was pleased to take them as it made him better. He was also willing not to eat chocolate, etc. because he said it was making him a naughty boy!

Simon enjoyed massage which we continued to do as regularly as we could at home. Simon also enjoyed his talks with imagery and looked forward to his sessions!

By attending Clover House we were encouraged to 'ignore the bad and praise the good' (which was not always easy). We began to gradually change ourselves in the way we handled Simon, trying to be more positive with him even when times were extremely hard.

We were warned by everyone things could get worse before they got better as Simon was detoxing from all the badness in his system caused by all the antibiotics he had been given over the years. Boy, did things go from bad to worse! So much so that I ended up with a black eye from Simon – this was in front of company! This was the only time I was reduced to tears by Simon's behaviour. I did in fact think how much more do we have to take. Even after tears and a black eye Simon showed no remorse whatsoever. However, this incident seemed to be the turning point, things seemed to improve gradually.

We are now at the stage where Simon will accept discipline. He is still hard work, but he is now more normal, his violence towards me has disappeared. He concentrates on his school work which he was having difficulty with before his time at Clover House. He is by no means an angel but how many boys are? The change in Simon has been noticed by people, they say he no longer has that nasty scowl on his face; he now listens when I speak to him and he seems a much happier little boy. One family member noticed such a change in Simon that she recommended another friend who was having difficulty with her children to speak to us about Simon and Clover House, and because of what they heard, they too started sessions at Clover House!

Why Clover House worked for Simon I do not know but it did and we are now beginning to enjoy Simon as a normal little boy, and we are able to take him out without worrying about him and be proud of him.

Our thanks go to everyone at Clover House for their support and help with Simon. He really has improved.

Chapter 33

Special Needs

Seventy five per cent of children who came to Clover House with special needs were significantly helped. They came with a variety of symptoms, the average starting score being 2.5/10 and finishing at 8.9/10.

The Problems

Dwain aged 10 was sponsored by the local women's refuge centre, having experienced violence in his parent's marriage. He had been a premature baby, and diagnosed as being developmentally delayed. His mother listed his problems with eating, behaviour, bedtime, asthma and bullying, which translated into scores of happy 2/10, eating 2/10, bullying 3/10, scared 3/10 and bedtime 5/10. His mother was distressed and angry having discovered that his one-to-one teacher had been angry with him for not learning. Dwain came with a big teddy bear for reassurance.

Adam aged 4 was also diagnosed with developmental delay, having been born a month premature. He had bad constipation, was moody, irritable, a poor sleeper, and a poor eater. Mum was depressed and exhausted over her own lack of sleep, and Dad used to dread coming home because Adam was so grumpy. They had been to the doctor and a paediatrician, and been prescribed laxatives, but constipation was still a problem. When Adam arrived at Clover House he had just had scarlet fever and was pale and lethargic and had conjunctivitis in his eyes. He was still in nappies, clutching his toy rabbit, and did not speak.

Rebecca aged 5. Since starting playgroup Rebecca had become worryingly violent and had physically hurt other children. She was having nightmares and had been placed on the special needs register at school for her behaviour. Mum was a nurse, and had taken her to the doctor, but reported that nothing could be suggested.

Nutrition

Dwain (10) was able to tell us his favourite foods were tuna, carrot and ice cream. His four-day food chart showed he just had toast for breakfast and lots of mugs of coffee. We had a lot of discussion about food, and gave them lots of handouts, with advice to avoid coffee and fizzy drinks, no peanuts or chocolate, and we advised that his parents should take more control of food.

At the second session Dwain's mother had bought a steamer and reported that she had bought fresh vegetables and had steamed them. The whole family had had bad colds/flu and everyone including the doctor was surprised that Dwain's asthma had not become worse.

They had cut out junk food, and kept to our advice. They were asked to continue this regime, and to do a star chart to add three different fruits a day to his diet, and to have salmon twice a week. We advised that they still needed to cut out chocolate and sweets completely.

At the next session we fine-tuned Dwain's eating plans and gave them motivation to continue the good work.

There was a difference in parental discipline, so we gave Dwain a routine to follow: breakfast after washing, eating at the table with no television; to change into casual clothes after school and play; then a bath, followed by bed and relaxing by reading with no television. Mother was committed and supportive of the changes in nutrition, even though Dwain said he wanted his junk food back.

Adam (4). Adam's mother was very interested in nutrition and took lots of handouts, and was keen to try new ideas. Homework was to have Aloe Vera juice, avoid cow's products and switch to goat's milk, or rice milk. We said no sweetcorn or pasta, but to try rice, pulses and legumes, and suggested getting a juicer.

After good reports at the second session, further advice included increasing Adam's green vegetable intake, making homemade chicken fritters, and no pre-packaged foods.

We prescribed Eskimo oils and reminded Dwain to drink more water, and to keep a food diary. His mother reported he had an aversion to fruit or anything he thought as messy food, so it was suggested they prepare smoothies and clear away any fruit peelings.

Rebecca (5). Although Rebecca's mother had previously taken control of her eating, she was back on oranges, fizzy drinks and chocolate. Our suggestion was to go back to basics, having sandwiches for lunch and a home cooked meal at night. We gave them children's multivitamins and Omega oils. Mother said that going back to basics and stopping school dinners had seen an improvement.

She was asked to continue with a food diary, and for Rebecca to try peas, cottage pie and more vegetables. We also gave them a star chart to encourage her not to eat her sister's chocolate and not to feel left out.

Massage

Dwain (10). We demonstrated a foot massage on Dwain at the first session, and he was keen to have a massage on his back. We gave him a flower remedy to take daily, a handout and massage oils for Mum to use at home.

As it was after Christmas and there had been a lot of upheaval, Mother had not felt up to doing their massage homework. We helped them choose a new flower remedy.

At the third session Dwain said he did not like his mother massaging him because her hands were wrinkly, so she was given plenty of oil and shown some cupping and chopping techniques which she practised, after which Dwain scored her 10/10.

However at the next session he had not let his mother massage him. Dad came next time; he was interested and asked a lot of questions. We suggested that if both parents presented a united front it would help Dwain. At the final and fifth session he had further massage and another flower remedy.

Adam (4). We demonstrated to Adam's mother how to massage his feet and tummy. Adam was receptive and became relaxed and content, and asked questions. Homework was to continue the massage at home concentrating on the reflexology points for constipation. We gave them a massage handout and oils. At the second session, they had done massage nearly every night, all going well. We had a chat at the fourth session about getting him out of nappies ready for school in a few months time.

Rebecca (5) had a foot massage and a flower remedy to help her anger, and mother was asked to do some at home. We demonstrated further massage techniques at the second session. Rebecca brought her toys with her, and told us that she liked boy's clothes (she never wore dresses), and played with boys. She had massages at home when she went to bed on time, enjoyed them and was disappointed if she did not have one.

Imagery

Dwain (10). A magic dice trick gained Dwain's attention and interest and he enjoyed the Babushka dolls and the story about one doll having an upset face, but that upsetting things happen but can then improve.

We installed the mountain lioness imagery, imagining being a lioness for confidence, and we could see a change in his features when he thought about it.

By talking to Dwain's mother, we were able to help her 'reframe' his developmental delay into his being very determined and focused to survive the trauma of his birth, and to enjoy his pleasing personality.

We used another magic trick at the second session, and they reported that Dwain had become angry while playing computer games. After some persuasion he admitted he got angry when he made a mistake and although he was given an example about riding a bike and having to keep trying, he argued about this.

He didn't do very well at trying the magic dice trick, so he tried again with advice on how to hold it, and we pointed out to everyone how well he managed after making a mistake.

Dwain became upset when the bullying was mentioned and denied it all. However he used crayons to set up the story and was helped to 'rewind' the incident (and clear the emotional element). Dwain then asked to tell another story, which was in fact the first one but with a lot more detail about teachers not knowing who to believe. Mum was amazed because she had not known about disagreement of school staff. This was again 'rewound' and a gentle version of the lioness was installed.

At the third session Dwain did his own magic trick to much positive response and encouragement. He used the crayons again to show what was happening about the bully at school. We told him a story about another child having a similar problem and giving the bully one last chance to play. A 'help frame' was set up for him to go back and grow up again as his 'younger' self. He was also having bad dreams so we installed a 'dream arm' and a 'super-hero' (to encourage lovely dreams) and he chose Scooby Doo. We did a further 'rewind' about his parents' problems.

At the fourth session we asked what else could be improved and he said, 'My mum and dad to disappear,' so this was reframed for them to argue less.

We asked if he is using the lioness technique we had shown him, and he clawed the air which made everyone laugh with pleasure. He said he often used it and it helped.

He then showed us examples of kick boxing, even though he was not learning it. We used crayons again to talk about an example of bullying – about the bully and friends taunting him about being 'special needs'. We sowed the seed that someone special was inside him to help when this happened. For his someone special he chose Jesus, so this idea was acted upon while he kept very still and quiet.

Dwain wasn't quite in the mood for work at his fifth and final session so we had a general chat.

Adam (10). We used the first session to make Adam feel welcome, especially as he was very shy. Adam had a problem using his potty, so we set up a connection with Thomas the Tank Engine, his favourite TV programme, and the potty, and interchanged how he felt about it.

At another session his potty problem was dealt with, the relaxed thoughts he has when watching 'Thomas the Tank Engine' were transferred to this thoughts about the potty. This technique was shown to mother to try again at home.

Rebecca (4) was shown the Babushka dolls, and we explained about her nightmare and a black rabbit. We gave her help by installing a 'dream arm' and a 'super-hero' (Batman) to always be available in her dreams to intervene before the dream got frightening.

When talking about getting in trouble at school, she said she did not like it when people did not tell the truth, so we discussed the idea that everyone, including herself, tells little white lies sometimes, and we thought about why some of the boys are telling lies. Because she gets into trouble with her responses to being hit, she practised ignoring it instead. A lioness was installed, and she was told to get inside the lioness whenever she needed courage and to practise it a lot.

At the second session Rebecca felt able to say she did not like her school because of the noise and the pressure. The second day in her new school was when it went wrong and she 'got into a tizz' about lunchtime. So a 'rewind' was completed on this, twice. Then we used the idea of helping someone else do imagery on going back and helping the younger Rebecca at that time. She sat quietly and as soon as the sequence was over she laughed.

At the third session she agreed she would work hard, and identified two selves, one angry and one who dealt with things. These were objectified as feelings outside, each with a visual symbol. One was a dark cloud, the other the sun shining. She was asked to watch them and say what happened. She described how they came together and the sun shone through the cloud. Then it was suggested that the cloud evaporate, leaving just a few wisps. This was checked twice for her feelings of anger. We also talked about stealing chocolate from her sisters, and we did a 'compulsion blow out' for clearing a habit.

Results

Dwain (10). By the second session Dwain's mother reported having enrolled on a nutrition course at the local college so that, in her words, 'she can make the whole family happy and healthy.'

Although his parents had separated over Christmas they reported at the fifth and final session that they were getting on better. Dwain had put on weight and throughout the sessions became more confident and chatty. They scored scared improved to 8/10, bullying 9/10, eating at 7/10 and happy 10/10.

Adam (4). By the second session Adam had changed from not talking to smiling and chatting and reported that all symptoms had improved. His mother said things had improved from day one when he started sleeping through the night, and therefore everyone was less irritable.

His grandmother saw him two weeks after his first treatment and said he was a totally different boy – happier, confident, outgoing.

Scores for toilet improved from 2 to 7/10, sleep 3 to 8/10 and moodiness from 4 to 9/10. Mum most liked 'having someone to listen properly and tackle the problems.'

Rebecca (5) had improved within the first week, her nightmares gone. The family reported they were doing everything by the book, which resulted in complete success. At the third and final session Rebecca was sleeping through the night, and her teacher had commented that she was much calmer at school and now playing nicely. They scored sleep from 4 to 9/10 and aggression from 2 to 8/10. She drew us a card of a flower and wrote, 'My best place to be to make me happy.'

Parent's Letter after treatment for Special Needs (Cerebral Palsy)

Dear Clover House,

By he time he was three years old, my little boy had been through a lot. He has 100 fits a day, a tube in his stomach to feed him, and for six months he vomited three times a day. Unable to sit up, I had been told, 'Be realistic, he will never talk or walk.'

After so much medical intervention it is easy to lose sight of the spirit of a child, and Patrick has plenty of spirit, especially determination. I knew I wanted to help him relax to help his spasms. So much had been done to his body, yet I knew if we could work with Patrick and find out what motivates him, then he could do anything. I wanted to engage his bright mind to help his body.

By chance I found out about Clover House and rang Basil. At once I felt supported and immediately the team,

Basil, Jill and Carole, saw the beauty of my son, and thankfully didn't even ask me to go through his long medical history.

Soon Basil got to the nub of the problem . . . if I wanted Patrick to relax, then I needed to be relaxed. So Basil actually began by working with me, and only then did I realise how crucial it was for me to be well. The last three years had taken their toll and both Patrick and I were the losers

Much of the help from Clover House has been practical – just what a mother wants! Jill has helped to relieve the problem of Patrick's constipation with foot massage. Carole has given us nutritional advice; when Patrick had trouble taking his vitamin tablets, she suggested juicing fruit and vegetables to get some good food into him.

Patrick enjoyed his visits to 'Clover House, with love inside'. This has been our experience.

Chapter 34

Trauma

Children who came to Clover House displayed a variety of symptoms that had occurred since being involved or witnessing traumatic incidents. These included being withdrawn, anger, sleep problems, tummy pains and anxiety.

There were no scores on trauma directly, but the average score of symptoms was initially 1.8/10 and improved to 7.2/10 over an average of 3.4 sessions.

The Problems

Amy aged 3. Although a bit young for Clover House, we never turn anyone away. Amy had been in a serious car crash a year ago, and had experienced her grandfather's death and separation from Mum due to Mum's hospitalisation. They had been referred to a consultant who suggested she was fine because she sat drawing a picture. Amy had previously been outgoing and happy, but since the accident she had become sad and insecure.

She went into her parent's bed about seven times a night, and was having nightmares. She did not talk to men – a man had rescued her out of the car; she was afraid to travel by car, and was not thriving at nursery school. Mum said she had sat in the doctors' surgery and cried her eyes out. She was at her wits end about the nightmares and felt she couldn't cope. She had been told Amy would grow out of it, and that you've got a naughty child, learn to deal with it.

Josie aged 5 had had a traumatic birth, and did not like nursery school. She had since witnessed her mother being struck down twice by a car. She had nightmares, did not get on with her brother, had trouble mixing with other children, had problems with listening and carrying out instructions, and was calling out and rolling around at school. Mum felt she was unhappy and insecure.

David aged 4 had been recommended by the local women's refuge centre. He had been upset about leaving his life behind – they had had to flee their home, leaving friends, family and pets – and he had been upset by an outburst by his father. He was also bedwetting.

Nutrition

Amy (3). Mum reported that Amy would eat until 2 pm, after that she would not eat at all, but was drinking a lot. Mum was asked to keep a food diary, and advised that they needed to take control of bad eating habits, with not so many addictive foods, and they were given ideas for better eating. By the second session Amy had tried chicken, peas, boiled egg, bacon and cheese on toast. We made further suggestions for her to try homemade cottage pie, omelettes, brown rice and brown bread. Her parents felt it was unfair for her not to have fizzy drinks or sweets, so we explained carefully about blood sugar levels.

Josie (5). Mother came in walking with the aid of a stick from the car crash. Because they were taking advice from a homeopathic friend, we could not interfere or change things. We did suggest having more vitamin B-based foods (i.e. brown bread, brown rice), and observed that Josie's diet seemed to be lacking in iron-based foods. Later Mum agreed to supplements of B complex and magnesium.

David (4). The family was short of time but were given handouts on nutrition to read. By the next session Mum was able to report that David was trying new foods and getting a reward of staying up an extra five minutes at bedtime. An elderberry tonic was prescribed, and we advised him to eat more fish, brown bread, lentils, pulses and cereals. At the next session they reported all homework had been done, and he had tried fish cakes, tuna, salmon, crab, sweetcorn, brown bread and mashed potatoes. We gave them increased motivation to continue with the good work.

Massage

Amy (3). Because Amy was only relating to Mum and rejecting everyone else, including her grandmother, she did not want massage. We suggested using lavender oil in the bath and on her pillow, and having a homeopathic remedy to help her sleep. We gave Mum a relaxation tape for children. To introduce Amy to the idea of reflexology, we recommended stroking her feet to begin with. By the next session, Mum had made a start with this. A flower remedy sheet was completed, and we demonstrated some gentle massage for Mum to continue at home.

Josie (5). Josie had previously had some osteopathy to stretch her which had been uncomfortable, which explained why she was nervous at seeing a couch in the massage room. We managed to establish some rapport, and were allowed to play with her feet to put her at ease.

Mum reported doing massage at home. At the second session Josie brought her toy rabbit who 'liked coming to Clover House'. Dad attended too and he got involved with massaging Josie. Mum also did a lovely massage and told Josie it would help her sleep more soundly.

At the next session Mum was worried that Josie was being very talkative to mask her feelings about the accident. Mum did a one-day massage course, and reported that Josie liked her massages. We asked if Mum had any help or support and she became tearful, and we suggested she go to the doctor to get some counselling for herself.

David (4). By using a teddy bear, we showed David what would happen with massage, and he was happy to get on the couch. Mum was shown some techniques, and we asked her to do some at bedtime or whenever possible, even if it was bits at a time. We gave her massage oils and a handout to read at home.

Imagery

Amy (3). We used a talking toy Eeyore donkey to make contact, and a 'rewind' on the car crash was done with Mum, with Amy listening in.

We showed Amy the Babushka dolls (where one of the dolls has an upset face and a story told how she was able to get over this), which she liked, and continued playing with.

As Amy liked painting, 'anchors' were made with painting and car travel, and 'collapsed'. Mum was shown how to do this.

Night time was still difficult because she was 'afraid of her room', and we did 'collapsed anchors' on fear and safety, and also with Mum who was finding nights frustrating. As they were going on holiday, we told Amy to take her monster with her and leave him on holiday!

Josie (5) re-enacted the car incident with toys with help to describe it without being involved, i.e. disassociated. Mum was given a 'rewind' on the incident twice, while Josie was asked to listen.

At the next session Josie was introduced to the Babushka dolls. She was concerned about the beginning of the car crash. Crayons were used for herself and Mum and a toy for the car. We made two attempts at using emotional freedom technique (EFT) which made Josie laugh. She then asked for a different coloured balloon to blow the ideas into.

We told her a story about an eight-year-old whose friends all held the dark blue balloons and let them go, carrying away their problems, the idea being that Josie was to visualise this happening for her.

At the next session Josie brought her brother along, and after some magic tricks, we did more work with Mum for Josie to listen in and hopefully do the work too.

Her brother said he had been having bad dreams, so we installed a 'dream arm' and a 'super-hero' to help him sleep. He was also experiencing some bullying, so a 'lioness' was installed to give him more confidence.

At the last session Josie was worried about being in the car in case any unusual incident occurred. She played with the car, and was shown how to do a switch using distance and size. She then wanted to play.

David (4) had a bad memory involving his Mum and Dad. As he was so young, they all did a 'rewind'. At the third session, both David and Mum said they are fine now, and Mum is coping well, so David was allowed to learn some magic tricks.

Results

Amy (3). By the second session Mum and Dad had lost weight, and bought a book on additives. Amy could travel in cars. At the third session she gave the imagery therapist (male) a hug and kiss goodbye, at which Mum was so astonished she said it was then she knew her daughter was going to be alright. She described it as having her normal daughter back. At the fourth session they scored eating habits improved from 0 to 7/10, being withdrawn from 2 to 10/10, men from 0 to 7/10 and cars 0 to 8/10.

Josie (5). At the third session, Josie scored her goals as school improved from 3/10 to 9/10; sleep 5/10 improved to 7/10; and brother 1/10 to 5/10. Mum wrote in a later evaluation that Josie 'was not so cross with herself and was able to deal with her emotions in a controlled way', and wrote that imagery and massage were 'excellent'.

David (4). By the third session Mum felt that the change in eating had helped enormously. She said that she herself was feeling better, and that David had appeared to have fully recovered from his ordeal, was sleeping well, no bedwetting, and he seemed much more relaxed. Their scores were confidence in Mum improved from 1 to 6/10 and new life 1 to 6/10.

Letter from Charlotte after treatment for Trauma
Dear Clover House,

When I was a baby I was born with a heart problem.
I spent about 2 years in hospital having operations to make
me better. I'm OK now, but when Mum heard about Clover
House, she thought it would be good for me if I went.

I couldn't understand this because I was better, but
I thought I would go and see what it was like when I got
there.

I thought it was meant for people who had an illness or
problem, and I thought I didn't have an illness or problem!
So I thought it was a stupid idea, but I decided to go.

I didn't like the people there to begin with. But when I
learned that I did have a problem I respected them more.
We talked about when I was a baby and I talked about
how I felt. We talked a lot about how Mum felt and I didn't
know how bad she felt and how upset she was about what
happened.

The people helped me a lot and I learned a lot of things
about when I was a baby. It was good getting it out in the
open.

Chapter 35

Aims and Conclusions

W e hope you have enjoyed reading about our work and experiences at Clover House. After almost twenty years of treating children and recording their case histories, of which we have included three for each of the 28 conditions, our aim is to share our knowledge and experiences for the benefit of others.

We also hope we have demonstrated that, by changing the increasingly modern diet of processed and packaged foods to a more consistent consumption of nutritious and natural foods, we can indeed heal the conditions, minds and behaviours of our children.

By finding time to give practical tender loving care through massage, we can also soothe and relax the mind and body. And by listening with compassion to the troubles, traumas, fears and concerns of these children, and using our three therapies, surprisingly quickly we can give them back the hope of a happy and healthy future.

We hope both parents and practitioners with children under their care, either at home or at work, have found some useful information in this book.

Our aim is to inspire you to put some of our methods into practice, and spread the word of the efficacy of complementary medicine.

So if we can help you to help more children, including by giving talks, workshops or training, then our aim will have been achieved.

Clover House
Complementary Therapy Centre for Children
447 Bath Road, Saltford, Bristol BS31 3AZ

Tel: 01225 344047
E-mail: info@cloverhouse.org
Website: www.cloverhouse.org

Index

* Denotes Chapters that include parents' letters